THE BLUE TRAIN

THE *Blue Train*

THE STORY OF

Anton Dolin

JOAN SELBY-LOWNDES

ABELARD-SCHUMAN
LONDON NEW YORK

Tw
4/9/70

ACKNOWLEDGMENTS

I WISH to express my acknowledgments to Cyril Beaumont for permission to use material from his *Complete Book of Ballets* published by Grossett & Dunlap; to Arnold Haskell for permission to quote from *Balletomania* and to Mr. J. Kirby for allowing me to describe one of his flying rehearsals.

I am most grateful to Messrs. Hodder and Stoughton for their help and cooperation with the *Peter Pan* chapters. Under Sir James Barrie's great literary bequest, the copyright of *Peter Pan* is vested in the Great Ormonde Street Children's Hospital in London; I wish to express my sincere thanks to the Governors of the Hospital for so kindly allowing me to make use of the material from the play.

I should like to thank Mr. Dolin for his help and cooperation with the book in manuscript and for checking the proofs, and, finally, my most grateful thanks go to his mother, Mrs. Healey-Kay, for the great assistance of her written records and personal reminiscences.

Library of Congress Catalog Card No.: 58-9112

Published by Abelard-Schuman Limited
London and New York

Printed in the United States of America

CONTENTS

1

The Family

A FLIGHT of startled birds wheeled up into the sky and circled over the tips of the trees clustered at the end of the garden. In the dusty shadows of the shrubbery below a thrush called shrill alarm. A violent rustling of leaves sent a nervous blackbird beak-first into the nearest holly bush, as a tree came suddenly to life, shaking its branches. High up a twig cracked and snapped.

"What a nuisance," said a clear, young voice inside the tree, and the piece of dead wood went rattling down to earth.

"You'll have to climb up the other side," said an older voice. "Can you reach it?" Philip Kay, directing operations from the ground, watched his young brother Pat, through the tangled, black pattern of branches overhead.

For answer came a scuffle of feet and a spatter of broken bark on his upturned face.

Over at the house the tall, garden windows were swung open and from the cool darkness of the living room came a slender figure, graceful and slim-waisted in her long, summer dress. A wide, flower-decked hat shaded her face. Mrs. Kay moved swiftly on to the lawn.

"Philip! Pat!" She looked around the deserted garden, wondering at her sons' gift for disappearing.

"Philip! Pat! Where are you?" Her voice reached them faintly.

"We're here, Mother," an invisible Philip answered, and a few moments later she saw the tousled figure of her oldest son materialize from a laurel bush.

"Oh, Phil!" She came up to him. "What are you doing?" Her soft, Irish voice was full of reproach. "Look at your clothes; that's your best school suit."

"I'm sorry, Mother, there wasn't time to change." He gave a half-hearted scrape at the assorted smears of green and brown. She couldn't be annoyed with him for long though, not on the first day of the summer vacation.

"What a boy." Her quick laughter forgave him. "Hardly arrived home and you're up to mischief already. What have you done with Pat now?"

"He's up there." Philip pointed in the general direction of the sky.

"Here I am!" The upper branches of the tree shook violently and parted. The mischievous, brown face of her second son Pat appeared among the leaves. "Watch me climb," he called down to her.

She waved gaily at him, but the color had suddenly drained from her face.

"Phil, you shouldn't let him climb a tall tree like that. Not by himself; he's such a little boy."

"That's the whole point," Philip explained carefully. "There's a nest up there and the branches wouldn't bear my weight."

"You and your birds' nests." She shook her head in despair.

"Pat won't fall," he consoled her. "He climbs like a monkey." He thrust his hands confidently into his pockets and together they watched the small figure wriggle his way up through the branches.

"I think I can reach it now," Pat announced, and the sight of him, balanced on tiptoe on a swaying branch, made his mother put her hand to her mouth as though to stop herself from crying out.

Slowly, a bare, sunburned arm reached up to the nest, cradled in the fork of two slender branches above his head. Small, strong fingers groped over the edge to the soft lining where the eggs nestled.

"There are four," Pat's clear voice called down.

"Take one only," the instructions came back, "and be careful not to break it."

To Mrs. Kay, anxiously waiting below, it seemed hours before a small boy in a crumpled sailor suit climbed out of the laurel bush, and a pale, speckled egg lay in Philip's hand.

"Look, Mother, isn't it a beauty?"

But she was too relieved to have Pat safely on the ground again to be able to admire it.

"Can I have it?" asked Pat.

"No, you can't. It's the only one I've got of this sort."

"I reached it, so I ought to have it."

"You wouldn't have known where the nest was if I hadn't shown you."

"Yes, I would."

"No, you wouldn't."

Mrs. Kay decided that a change of subject was due.

"Pat, dear." She pulled her resisting small son towards her and tried to pick some of the bits of twig and leaves out of his hair. "Have you been for a swim today?"

"No, Mother." He wriggled impatiently. They weren't finished with the egg after all. "Can't I have it because it's my birthday?"

"It isn't your birthday," said Philip.

"It will be—not tomorrow, but the next day. Won't it, Mother?"

"Yes, darling, it will—July 27th." She made an attempt to straighten out the sailor suit. "Perhaps Philip will give you another egg for a present."

"I want *that* egg." Tears were threatening. Young Pat certainly knew what he wanted.

"I tell you what," said Philip. "We'll go bird-nesting on your birthday, and you can have all the eggs we find."

"Can we really?"

"Yes, it's a promise."

And, since Pat adored his older brother, the bad moment passed and he was happy again. Besides, with this talk of birthdays, a new idea had presented itself.

"Mother, you said when I was eight I could have a bicycle."

"Yes darling, I did."

"I'm going to be eight the day after tomorrow."

"Yes, I know you are."

"Will I have a bicycle?"

"You must wait and see."

"If I have a bicycle on my birthday, can I take it to go bird-nesting?"

"You've got to learn to ride it first," said Philip.

"Is it difficult?"

"Father will teach you." Mrs. Kay gave up the crumpled suit as a bad job. "That reminds me, I wanted to know what you two boys were doing this afternoon. Father and I have to go out, and Anthony wants to go swimming."

"I'll take him." Pat, aged seven, considered he was quite grown-up enough to look after Anthony, aged four.

"No, darling, you know you musn't go swimming alone." She was looking hopefully at Philip.

"I was going up to the schoolroom to rearrange my eggs," he said.

"Can I come and help?" Pat promptly inquired. He would give up even swimming if he could stay with his adored, older brother.

"Haven't you got something else you'd rather do?"

Pat hesitated, and then seemed to make up his mind.

"Yes, I have," he said rather loudly, and went trotting across the lawn.

"Pat! Come back!" his mother called out, but the independent, small figure disappeared around the corner of the house. "Oh, Phil, dear, you might have told him that he could stay," she reproached him. "You know he loves being with you, and he's done nothing but count the days till you came home."

"He's such a nuisance in the schoolroom," said Philip. "He can never stay still for two minutes together."

"Couldn't you do your eggs later on?" she coaxed him. "I don't want to spoil your first day at home, but I'd feel much happier about going out if I knew that Pat and Anthony were with you."

"All right." Philip, who really loved his two baby brothers a great deal more than his birds' eggs, smiled at her, and gave up his idea. "I'll take them to the beach," he promised.

It was a promise he was not to keep, however. Mr. and Mrs. Kay, on their way to Bognor, were happily unaware that poor Philip was running around the garden in search of two elusive small boys who had completely vanished.

"Pat! Anthony!" he called, but the garden, drowsing in the hot afternoon sunshine, lay mysteriously silent. "Little beasts must be hiding in the house." Philip gave up the garden search and went muttering indoors.

A bush near the front gate moved. A cautious head peeped out.

"He's gone." The rest of Pat climbed out, followed by Anthony, the youngest of the family.

"Come on." Pat caught hold of his brother's chubby wrist. "Run."

Out of the gate they went and down the lane; two small figures trotting along between the high, green hedges. Anthony's face soon turned red in the heat; he began to lag behind.

"Why do we have to run away from Phil?" he wanted to know.

"Because he doesn't want us with him." Pat looked around to make sure they were not being followed, and slowed down to a walk. "He wants to go and be with his eggs by himself, so we'll go to the beach on our own." And, as Anthony did anything Pat wanted, they went.

The beach at Felpham was a long, golden stretch of sand cut by wooden breakwaters. Dotted over the sands, little girls, in floppy sunbonnets and white dresses, played with pails and shovels. Little boys in wide, straw hats and sailor suits made sand-castles, while their nurses, very stiff and buttoned up, kept an eye on their charges, or mothers in long, graceful dresses sat under shady parasols.

Pat and Anthony made their way down to the water's edge. They took off their sandals and went running through the curly, shallow waves, shouting and kicking up the silvery spray. They fished for crabs, and looked for treasures among the shells in the wet sand.

"Oh Anthony, look at that." Pat's attention was suddenly caught by a noisy group of big boys playing near a breakwater. They turned somersaults, and played leapfrog, and suddenly one was standing up on his hands.

Fascinated, Pat started to run towards them, but long before he got there the group had broken up and raced away.

"I'm going to see if I can do that." Pat put his hands on the sand, kicked his legs in the air—and fell over, sideways.

"It's not as easy as it looks," he informed Anthony who stood gravely watching him. Next time he fell over on the other side.

"What are you doing?"

Pat sat up. A dark-eyed little girl about his own age was standing quite close, looking at him as though he were a very strange animal.

"I want to stand on my hands." Pat tried again. This time he kicked too hard and fell over on his back.

"Let me try." Anthony, in faithful imitation, put his small behind in the air, but only managed to get one leg off the ground.

"What do you want to do that for?" the small girl asked.

"I want to see what it feels like," Pat told her. "Can you stand on your hands?"

"No." She shook her head.

"I climbed a tree today," said Pat. "Can you climb trees?"

"No. We don't have any trees at home."

"No trees?" Pat frowned. "How funny. Where do you live?"

"In London. It's all houses and streets."

"We live here." Anthony gave up his handstands and sat down.

"Why do you live in London?" Pat wanted to know.

"I don't know." She shrugged her shoulders. "My mother brought me there from our home in Hungary. It's a country far away from here. We traveled for days and nights in the train, and crossed the sea and I was sick . . ."

"What's your name?" interrupted Anthony, who wasn't interested in travel talks.

"Maria. What's yours?"

"Anthony."

"I'm Pat. We're brothers. How old are you?"

"I'm ten." She twirled around on one foot.

"I'm going to be eight the day after tomorrow," Pat told her. "I'm going to have a bicycle for my birthday. Have you got a bicycle?"

"I'm not allowed to have one."

"Why not?"

"Because of my dancing. I'm going to be a dancer when I grow up." She turned around on the other foot. "In London I have lessons every day." She swung out a long, straight leg and arched her foot.

"Dancing lessons?" Pat was interested. This sounded much more exciting than the reading and arithmetic lessons he had at school. "Do you like it?"

"I love it. I never want to do anthing else." She danced about on her toes.

"What do you learn?"

"Ballet dancing of course."

"What's that?"

"I can't explain." She shrugged her shoulders, and her arms swept up into a graceful curve. "You must see it to understand."

"Dance something now," Pat demanded, and the small girl did a series of elementary ballet movements. Her full white dress flew out around her slim, golden-brown legs. She was very pretty and very graceful.

"I like that." Pat watched her carefully. "I can do it too."

"No, you can't."

"Why not?"

"Because you have to be taught how to hold your arms and legs."

"Well I can jump in the air higher than you did."

"Come on then, we shall see." They went running and dancing across the wet sand in a series of unrecognizable grands jetés.

"There, I told you I could jump higher than you." They stopped, out of breath.

"That's because you're a boy."

"I think I'd like to learn dancing." Pat looked at her. "Dance some more," he said, but someone was calling.

"That's my mother." Maria turned and waved. "I must go." She went dancing away from him across the sands, her black hair flying out. Pat walked slowly and thoughtfully back to Anthony.

He was never to see little Maria from Hungary again, but the idea she had put into his head was never to leave him.

2

The Package

A BIG delivery truck came rumbling slowly along the lane, reluctantly pulled by a fat, brown horse.

"Whoa!" said the driver.

The horse didn't need to be told twice.

"Lazy lump of fat." As the driver climbed down he sent a malevolent look at his horse who was already nodding in the shafts. "Not much chance you'll run away." He heaved a large crate on to his shoulders and went stumping along the path to the house.

"Package here for Kay." The driver blew heavily through his overhanging mustache.

"Well I never!" Rosie, the maid, stood on the doorstep gaping at the large crate on his shoulder.

"Is this the house?"

"That's right." Rosie's starched cap nodded vigorously.

"Where am I to put it?"

"Oh! The mistress didn't say."

"Well I ain't goin' to wait with this here package on me back all afternoon while you make up your mind, see."

"It seems a bit large, but if it's a package I suppose it had better go in the hall same as the letters."

The driver dumped his offering at the foot of the stairs.

Rosie fled into the kitchen to see if cook thought she'd done the right thing, while up in the schoolroom in the far corner of the house, Philip, surrounded by trays of birds' eggs, remained happily deaf to the banging of doors, the scrunch of steps, and the distant sound of the truck's horse moving reluctantly away.

In the hall, the large grandfather clock looked with disapproval at the intruding crate.

"Grrr!" it remarked, and, getting no reaction, struck five extra loudly.

Down on the beach, children, baby carriages, and nurses were on the move.

"Come on, Anthony, we'd better go home." Pat caught hold of his brother's hand.

The long, sandy lane that led from the beach was sheltered and stifling. Anthony's short legs soon tired, and his feet dragged more and more slowly in the dust.

"Come on." Pat pulled him.

Anthony sat down in the middle of the lane.

"You can't stay there," said Pat indignantly.

"Yes I can. Anthony's tired. Want Mommy."

"You can't have her, she's at Bognor." Pat tried to pull him up. "Come on, it isn't far now."

"You carry me," suggested Anthony, but Pat had a better idea.

"Aren't you hungry?" he suggested.

Anthony thought about this.

"It must be tea-time," Pat went on. "Cook said she might make chocolate cake today, and if we're late we won't get any."

"Chocolate cake!" Anthony rapidly forgot he was tired. Hand in hand, they made good progress back to the house.

The hall was cool and dim after the bright sunshine outside. The light, filtering through a stained window, spilled untidy pools of red and green on the wooden crate standing at the foot of the staircase.

The patter of boys' sandals on the tiled floor stopped abruptly.

"Look at that!" Pat pointed.

"What is it?" Anthony hung back, afraid it might come to life and bite.

Pat tiptoed cautiously up to it. He looked at the labels pasted on the outside. There was no mistaking what the crate contained. The promise had come true. He fingered the rough wood and tingles of excitement shivered up and down his back.

"It's come."

"What has?" Anthony advanced cautiously.

"It's my bicycle. Mother promised I'd have one for my birthday and this is it." In rising excitement Pat's fingers explored the gaps between the slats, trying to feel the shape of this exciting, hidden thing under the brown paper.

A sudden noise made him jump and whip his hands behind his back. The green baize door from the kitchen regions shuffled open. Rosie's face appeared.

"Oh! It's you, Master Pat and Master Anthony. I thought I heard the front door. You're late for tea. Now then, you leave that package alone. Don't you dare lay a finger on it."

Anthony looked at her doubtfully and put his finger in his mouth, but Pat's small, tense body didn't move. He didn't even look in her direction.

"You're not to touch it. Do you hear?"

Pat went on looking at the crate.

"Rude boy." She sniffed and the green baize door sighed

itself shut. In the silence that followed the muffled tap of Rosie's retreating feet, the tick of the grandfather clock repeated loudly, "Don't touch. Don't touch."

Pat and Anthony looked at each other.

"Where's Philip?" asked Anthony.

"Philip! Of course. I wonder if he's seen it?" And the idea sent Pat suddenly chasing up the stairs.

"Philip!" His voice woke the echoes. "Philip? Where are you?" The sound of his feet pounding along the corridor broke the stillness of the house.

"Philip!" called Anthony in shrill imitation.

"Philip, it's here, it's arrived." Pat burst into the schoolroom. "My bicycle, it's downstairs, in the hall. You must come and see."

No time for Philip to say, "Where have you been" and "Be careful of the eggs"; he was swept up in the general excitement and came racing down the stairs with them.

"But there's nothing to see," said Philip when he caught sight of the crate.

"Oh yes, there is." Pat began pulling at one of the slats.

"I don't think you ought to touch it," said Philip doubtfully, "anyway not till Mother and Father come back."

"I only want to look at it." Pat had managed to wrench off a thin slat.

"You'll get into awful trouble."

"Never mind." Pat was recklessly tearing at the shrouding paper. "Please come and help." He pulled away a handful of straw packing and more paper. "Look!" The silvery curve of a handlebar stood revealed.

The sight of the treasure within reach was too much for Philip. He pulled out his penknife and got to work.

Wood cracked and split, nails creaked, as the slats were

ripped off. Pat and Anthony tore away the paper wrappings. Straw and wood-shavings spilled over the hall floor. No holding back now. They tore off the last cocoons of protecting paper, and there, in the wreckage of the crate stood the gleaming new bicycle. It was shining black with a fine red line; silvery wheels and handlebars; and a shining leather saddle.

"It's a beauty," said Philip, and Pat wheeled it around the hall. The new rubber tires made soft squeaking sounds on the tiles.

"What would happen if I got on?" He stroked the saddle thoughtfully.

"You'd fall off," said Philip.

"Wouldn't you hold it for me; just so that I could see what it's like?" he pleaded.

"Not in here."

Pat wheeled the gleaming bicycle out of the front door and down the step into the drive. Philip hoisted him into the saddle.

"It's just the right size for you."

"Let's go down the drive, just a little way."

"Hang on tight then." Philip held him up, and, with one hand on the handlebars and one on the back of the saddle he pushed off.

The procession went wobbling down to the gate, Anthony trotting along in the rear.

"We'll try the lane," suggested Philip. "It's less bumpy."

Up and down they went.

"Let go of the handlebars," said Pat, as they turned to go up the lane a second time. "I want to steer myself." So Philip held on to the saddle and went jogging alongside while Anthony sat in the grass on the bank and watched.

"I think it's lovely," Pat called out as the pedals spun around easily under his feet, and he watched the silver spokes of the front wheel flashing around. "I'd like to do this forever."

"I'm sure you would." Philip was getting out of breath and very hot. "But I'm going to stop for a minute."

"How do you stop?"

"Put the brakes on and steer for the side." Philip helped to ground the bicycle gently against the bank.

"Get off a minute while I rest," he said.

"Don't want to. Look, I can stay on by myself." Pat propped himself up with one foot on the bank.

"Well don't fall off and scratch the paint." Philip flopped down on the grass beside Anthony.

Pat rocked the bicycle back and forth, wondering what it felt like to ride alone. He stretched a leg down as far as it would go.

"I can almost put my foot on the ground," he announced. but Philip, who was playing with Anthony, didn't hear.

"I'll try a little way," Pat said to himself. "One, two, three—go." A strong push off the bank, and he was launched. His feet scrabbled on the pedals, the bicycle wobbled violently, but they were still moving; he hadn't fallen off. The wobble was almost under control. This was wonderful. He was getting his balance.

"Look, Phil! Anthony, look!" he shouted. "I'm riding it by myself."

He clutched the handlebars tightly, and, keeping his eyes on that wavering front wheel, steered a precarious course down the lane.

"Hi! Pat! Where are you going?" Philip's voice sounded a long way behind him. "Come back."

"I can ride! I can ride a bicycle all by myself," Pat shouted as he wobbled around the bend, and he rode it—straight into the arms of his returning parents.

3

First Appearance

"I STILL SAY that the boy should have had a good whipping." Mr. Kay, dressed for dinner, came in to see if his wife was ready. "You're too soft with him, Maude, that's the trouble."

"You have taken his bicycle away and sent him to bed early; don't you think that's punishment enough?" She was sitting at the dressing-table putting finishing touches to her hair.

"But the sheer impudence of it—breaking open the crate. Never saw such a mess as the hall was in, and then taking the thing out and riding it . . . " The enormity of the offense seemed to choke him.

"I think it was so clever of him to be able to ride it," said Mrs. Kay thoughtfully. "He must have an amazing sense of balance. I think he must inherit it from you," her gentle voice went on. "Do you remember the first time you put him on a horse? You remarked then that he had an extraordinary sense of balance."

Mr. Kay grunted, and came over to the mirror to see if his tie was straight. He wasn't ready yet to admit that, secretly, he too was rather proud of his naughty son.

Meanwhile, the subject of this conversation, shut away in the boys' bedroom at the end of the house, bounced around under the blankets and got his pajamas twisted into a corkscrew around his wriggling body.

In the bed in the far corner of the room, Anthony, tired out with his day's adventures, was fast asleep. "Lucky thing," thought Pat, as he looked at the still lump under the bedclothes and heard his brother's quiet breathing. It made him feel more wide awake than ever.

Outside it was still light; a soft evening light that filtered through the closed curtains. Pat kicked the blanket back, waved his legs in the air, and thought how horrid it was to have to be in bed.

He stared at the patterned wallpaper and saw again the scene downstairs: his father, stiff with angry disapproval, wheeling the bicycle; Philip and Anthony, very subdued, walking behind; and his mother keeping close to him and saying nothing. There had been worse to come when they reached the wreckage of straw and paper in the hall. There was Rosie's horrified face repeating over and over again, "I told them to be sure and not touch it," his father's stern voice ordering him off to bed, and his own tears of rage.

"I shall take the bicycle away and lock it up," his father had said, "and if you don't behave yourself, I shall give it to another little boy, and you will never see it again."

No more bicycle! Pat, however, was neither frightened nor subdued by threats. He thought his father was being unfair, and his Irish temper had come bubbling up inside him.

"No," he had yelled, "it's my bicycle," and he had gone running backwards on the tips of his toes, screaming at the top of his voice.

"Pat, be quiet." But his father's voice had had no effect, and Pat had yelled louder than ever.

"Pat!" He had felt his mother's arm go around him, and he had known by the look on her face that fighting would do him no good. Fair or not, he had to accept his father's decision. So, the angry tears had dried on his cheeks and his mother had taken him upstairs to have supper in disgrace in the schoolroom while she bathed Anthony, and then he had been sent to bed.

"Anyway I rode it," Pat defiantly kicked his legs up and pedaled an imaginary bicycle along the road. He didn't hear the door softly open.

"Pat! You bad boy! What are you up to now?" It was his mother's soft voice. "You should have been asleep long ago."

Her long evening dress rustled as she came into the room and the air was suddenly sweet with the warm fragrance of her perfume. She leaned over Anthony's bed, smiling to see him happily asleep with a teddy bear hugged in his arms.

"I can't go to sleep." Pat straightened himself out. "What time it it?"

"It's about eight o'clock." She came and sat on his bed, the full skirts of her dress spreading their pale green folds of shining silk over the tumbled blankets. "What are we going to do with such a bad boy?" She pushed back the hair from his hot forehead.

"Mother!" Pat fingered the long, colored fringe of the shawl she wore. "Did Father really mean what he said about giving my bicycle away? I will really have it on my birthday, won't I?"

"You wait and see." She tried not to smile at the sight

of his anxious face. "But remember, you've got to be good until then. No more playing truant either, running down to the beach."

She straightened the bedclothes and bent to kiss him good night. Two very wide awake brown eyes watched her go.

"Good night, darling," she called softly from the door.

"Mother."

"What is it?"

"Can I have dancing lessons?"

"Dancing lessons? What for?"

"I met a little girl on the beach today who dances, and I want to be a dancer too when I grow up."

"We'll have to see. You just go to sleep now." Mrs. Kay went downstairs wondering at the curious ideas children get into their heads.

Bed was duller than ever after she had gone. Pat lay on his back and looked at the cracks in the ceiling over his head. He thought of the girl with dark hair who danced. He remembered the glorious feeling of running and jumping with her, flying through the air in great big leaps.

The sound of the gong reverberated through the house and from below came the sudden hum of voices. That would be Father and Mother and everybody going into the dining room. He's forgotten to ask who was coming to dinner to-night. He wondered what Father had said to Philip about the bicycle business. He wondered when Philip would be coming up to bed. Not for hours and hours if they were just starting dinner. It was funny how one got sleepy all of a sudden.... He didn't really want to go to sleep... he wanted to tell Philip about that girl on the beach. How pretty she looked when she stood on her toes and went twirling round and round . . . and round . . . and round . . .

The distant, cascading notes of a piano wove their way insistently into the pattern of his dreams The rise and fall of the melody turned into shapes, circles, and curving lines, breaking and re-forming. Now it shifted into a picture of a girl with flying dark hair on a shining bicycle; her feet whirling round and round making the wheels spin faster and faster. He must catch her, he must run after her, but the music held him back. Faster, if only the music would hurry and let him catch up . . . With a jerk, Pat opened his eyes. The room was swimming in shadows, shadows that still moved. He frowned; he had been dreaming, but he could still hear music. It was real. He sat up and the corners of the room came into focus, taking solid shape. What time was it? He looked across at Philip's bed. There was the familiar mound in it. It must be quite late.

"Phil." He called softly, but the tousled, dark head on the pillow didn't move.

Still the music went on. Pat was wide awake now, listening. It must be his mother. She often played in the evening to entertain her guests. Sometimes when they were alone, she played for him. He never tired of listening to the lovely sounds she drew out of the piano, sounds that sent tingles of excitement all over him, and made him want to move, to jump and wave his arms. It was impossible to lie still now.

Pat got out of bed and tiptoed to the door. Softly, very softly, he turned the handle and pulled it open. The music suddenly poured through the gap.

Just across the corridor, directly in front of him, was the door that opened on to a flight of stairs curving down into the music room below. Drawn irresistibly by those dancing notes, he crept down. Peeping through the banisters now, he could see the piano below, its top opened like a great bird's wing to let out those flying, golden notes.

His mother had her back to the stairs. He could see her slender fingers which seemed to dance over the white and black keys. Watching her, and absorbed by her music, Pat was quite unaware of the still circle of people sitting in armchairs grouped around the open windows at the far end of the room.

Noiselessly he ran down the last few steps on to the wide expanse of polished floor. His bare feet made no sound as he danced, a small, ghostly figure in white pajamas. Like a puppet pulled by invisible strings, he let the music shape the movements of his body.

There was a slow stir among the silent group of listeners. Someone had caught sight of that dancing white figure behind the piano. A second head turned, and a third. Glances were exchanged, and smiles.

At the piano, Mrs. Kay swiftly sensed that the quiet spell was broken. Her fingers faltered and stopped. Mr. Kay, whose head had been quietly nodding on his chest, woke with a guilty start. He looked around and saw, to his horror, the small figure of his son, who had been sent to bed in disgrace hours ago, capering around in the middle of the music room.

Mr. Kay was a man of action. Things happened swiftly. The apparition in white pajamas was rapidly and forcefully removed. In the seclusion of the upper corridor, a sound spanking took place, and a subdued small boy crept back into his bed.

So ended the first public appearance of Pat Kay, dancer.

4

Hove

"WHAT IS this idea of Pat's that he wants to dance?" Mr. Kay wanted to know. It was after lunch and they were sitting by the open French windows of the living room.

"It seems that on the beach the other day he met a little girl who is going to be a dancer, and now he wants to do the same thing." Mrs. Kay, bending over her sewing, smiled as she listened to the distant shouts and laughter of her three sons playing in the sunlit garden. "He's quite serious about it."

"Nonsense." Mr. Kay rattled his newspaper indignantly. "Who ever heard of a boy wanting to dance?"

"I think it's just that he loves anything that makes him run."

"Aren't games good enough for him, football and tennis?" Mr. Kay dismissed dancing as a low form of amusement.

"You know he loves all games and sports," Mr. Kay agreed, "but he's got this idea that he wants to dance, too. After all he does love music."

"Ridiculous." He went back to *The Times*.

Mrs. Kay said no more, and, busy over her sewing, wondered again at the strange ideas of boys. She raised her head to watch those three sons of hers playing on the lawn like puppies. "Do look at them." She laughed. "Pat is doing a dance and the others are copying him."

"It's time that boy went off to boarding school," said Mr. Kay fiercely over the top of his paper. "That'll knock the nonsense out of him. Dancing indeed!"

"I don't doubt it's just a passing fancy," said Mrs. Kay mildly. "He'll grow out of it. After all he is only eight."

Pat didn't grow out of it. The desire to dance remained, but there was no dancing school at Felpham and nothing could be done about it. So the desire remained unexpressed, half forgotten in the crowded days of childhood.

For two years, life went on much as usual in the house at Felpham. Mrs. Kay saw Philip quickly growing up into a tall, broad-shouldered, serious member of the senior class; while little Anthony was suddenly no longer a baby, but a sturdy schoolboy; and in between them her mischievous son Pat, already a vivid personality with a will of his own. He, more than the others, had inherited his mother's temperament. Impulsive, generous, quick to laughter or tears; the Irish strain ran strong in him, and perhaps for that reason he was closer to her, for she, better than anyone, understood his naughtiness, his fierce independence; the swift, strange moods that came to him, even as a small child, when he needed to be alone. She feared what the discipline of boarding school would do to this proud, free spirit.

Happily, the time for that had not yet come, and Pat attended the local school. He took solemn charge of Anthony each morning, pushing his unwilling small brother down the road, and keeping a fatherly eye on his activities until he brought him safely home again. The pair of them would count the days until vacation should bring Philip home once more, and all three could romp their way through the glorious days of freedom.

So, school terms and vacations followed each other in the safe, ordered life of pre-war England. From time to time disquieting paragraphs appeared in the papers about the armed strength of Germany and her growing fleet; ugly rumors that were quickly dismissed and forgotten by most people.

"We won't have war," they said; and Mrs. Kay, whose home, husband, and three growing sons happily filled her life, agreed with them.

Then, early in 1914, something else came along to occupy her thoughts. Grandfather Healey became Family Problem Number One. Mrs. Kay's father was a widower and an old man.

"I do think he needs someone to look after him properly." Mrs. Kay, just back from a visit to her father at Hove, was pouring out family tea. "He doesn't look at all well."

"He's got that housekeeper person, hasn't he?" said Mr. Kay.

"Yes, but she finds him very difficult to manage nowadays. Pass the muffins, Phil, dear." She pointed to the big, covered dish warming in front of the fire. "I feel that one of the family ought to be with him."

"Can't he come and live with us?" suggested Mr. Kay.

"I wish he could, but you know he'd never come here; there's no railroad."

Pat decided that the conversation was getting interesting.

"Why does Grandfather have to have a railroad?"

"He likes to see the trains go past." Mrs. Kay handed around the jam. "That's why he took this house at Hove. The railroad goes along the edge of the garden."

"He's been in bed for years," added Mr. Kay.

"What was the matter with him?" Philip asked.

"Nobody knew." Mrs. Kay passed the cakes. "He just decided to go to bed one day, and he's been there ever since. It's a long time now—let me see. Pat was quite a baby. It must be nearly nine years."

"Do you mean, he's been in bed for nine years without being ill?" Pat was horrified.

"Shall we say he is suffering from old age," his mother explained. "Now, who's going to finish the toast?" She passed the plate to her hungry family. "His housekeeper complains nowadays that his room is getting so full of birds and cages that she spends all her time cleaning up after them, and he orders her about as though she were a regiment of soldiers . . ." She glanced up at the big, gold-framed portrait of her father that hung on one side of the fireplace. It was difficult to imagine that the eccentric old man, living alone in his house at Hove, had once been the handsome, dashing young cavalry officer whose clear, blue eyes looked steadily out from the painted canvas.

"That's Grandfather, isn't it?" Anthony pointed to the picture.

"Yes, darling, but he doesn't look like that any more. He's a very old man now. That was painted a long time ago just after he was married. The picture of my mother was done about the same time."

They all gazed up at the portrait of the lovely young Irish girl that hung on the other side of the fireplace.

"She's my grandmother then." Anthony worked out the relationship.

"That's right. She never saw you though. She died many years before you were born."

"And Grandfather's lived by himself ever since." Pat summed up the family story.

"That's about it." Mrs. Kay smiled.

"Must do something about the old fellow," Mr. Kay decided. "Can't leave him there all alone if he's not being looked after properly."

Something was done about Grandfather Healey. Since he wouldn't come to them, they had to go to him. So, early in the spring of 1914, while Philip was away at school, the Kay family uprooted itself from Felpham and went to live at Hove.

They exchanged their quiet, country house for the racket of trains running past the edge of Grandfather Healey's long, narrow strip of garden.

"No interesting birds' nests around here," said Philip gloomily when he came home for the Easter vacation. "Not with all these noisy trains." Pat and Anthony were showing him around the garden.

"You don't notice them after a while," said Pat, who was already getting used to his new life in a seaside town.

"What's your new school like?" Philip wanted to know.

"It's all right." Neither Pat nor Anthony could raise any enthusiasm for the process of being educated. One school was much like another.

"I want to go to a dancing school and have lessons," added Pat. "There are places here that teach it, but Father and Mother won't let me go."

"Dancing?" Philip stared at him. "What on earth do you want to learn that for?"

They were interrupted by the sound of a window opening, and a stentorian shout.

"That's Grandfather." Pat hastily straightened his suit and smoothed his hair.

"It's Saturday morning," added Anthony as he pulled up his socks.

"What about it?" asked a perplexed Philip.

"We have to go into his room on Saturday mornings." Pat tied a stray shoelace. "It's a parade."

"Won't be long," Anthony called back as they ran indoors.

Their mother was waiting for them outside Grandfather's bedroom door.

"Are you nice and neat?" She looked them over. "In you go then."

They opened the door.

There was a whir and a flutter of wings. As two rather awed small boys walked in, birds flew off in all directions. In the middle of the room Grandfather Healey sat up in a big bed, looking very fierce. All around the walls and on the furniture were rows and rows of bird cages. Their doors stood wide open so that the inmates were free to fly in and out as they pleased.

Pat and Anthony, well trained by this time in their parade routine, lined up beside the bed, standing very stiffly.

"Shoulders back," barked Grandfather. "Heads up. Heels together." He looked them up and down, his blue eyes very stern under bushy, white eyebrows.

The birds, scattered over the room, perching on cages, pictures, and curtain rails, twittered and looked on.

"Very good. Parade dismiss."

Pat and Anthony relaxed. Grandfather groped among the clutter of things on the table beside him. The boys held out their hands and each received an orange, a biscuit, and two cents.

"Thank you, Grandfather."

"Well! What are you waiting for now?" he barked at them.

"Will you make your birds fly for us?" asked Pat who was not in the least afraid of the gentle old man who pretended to be so fierce.

"You like them, do you?"

"Yes. I'd like to have a bird of my own and teach it to do things the way you do."

"You would, would you?" He looked hard at Pat. "How old are you?"

"I'm nearly ten."

"Well, perhaps I'll give you a bird one day."

"Thank you, Grandfather."

"Can I have one too?" asked Anthony.

"Not yet. You're too young. Wouldn't look after it properly. Now go over there and stand very still," Grandfather commanded.

The two boys tiptoed to the corner by the door. The old man crumbled some biscuit in his hand and whistled softly. His birds cocked their heads on one side, listening. Bright, round eyes watched the tempting handful of crumbs. He whistled again. There was a flutter, a little whir of feathers, and there was a chaffinch perched on one of Grandfather's big, gnarled fingers. A bullfinch took courage and landed on his thumb. In a few minutes a whole lot of little birds were hopping around on his hand and arm, pecking crumbs. There was a gentle, faraway look on the old man's face as he watched them. He had forgotten all about his small grandsons. After a few minutes they tiptoed softly out of the room.

"Their mother was waiting for them in the passage.

"What are you going to spend your money on this week?" she asked them as they showed her their treasures.

"Don't know." Pat jingled his two pennies.

"Candy," said Anthony promptly. "Let's go down to the candy store now. Philip hasn't seen it yet. Can we go?"

"Yes, darling, if you like."

"I'll get Philip." Anthony went running into the garden, but Pat lingered.

"And what's my Pat going to do today?" Mrs. Kay put her arm around him.

"We're going to show Philip around." Pat thoughtfully nibbled the corner of his biscuit. "Mother?" He looked up suddenly. "There's a house down the road that says 'dancing lessons' on a board outside. Couldn't I go and learn dancing there next term?"

"You are a strange boy." She stroked his hair. "Still this idea of dancing. Wouldn't you rather be good at games?"

"Why can't I do both?" he asked. "I want to dance too."

"It won't work, darling; you know Father doesn't like the idea."

"Why won't he let me?" Pat looked at the ground, his eyes clouding with gathering tears. "I know if you asked him really hard he'd say yes. Please make him say yes."

"Suppose you try and forget all about this dancing idea," she suggested. "You just say to yourself that you're going to grow up into a big, strong man who can run faster and play games better than anyone else."

"But I want to learn to dance, too." The angry tears were blinding him. "Other people dance, so why can't I? It isn't fair." Pat broke away from her and went running out of the house.

"It is extraordinary," Mrs. Kay was saying to her husband

in the study, a few minutes later. "He's got this idea in his head and he won't give it up."

The front door banged and through the window she watched the three boys going down the road to the candy store. "I wonder if we wouldn't be wise to let him have dancing lessons, since his heart is so set on it. After all it can't do him any harm."

"Waste of time and money," said Mr. Kay from his armchair.

"A few lessons wouldn't cost very much," she persisted. "He'll probably realize that it's not at all what he thinks it is, and it'll cure him of ever wanting to dance again."

And Mr. Kay, who was thoroughly sick of Pat and his dancing, finally agreed.

5

First Dancing Lessons

OUTSIDE A HOUSE in Hove, a painted signboard announced "Miss Clarice James's Dancing Academy." Here, one Saturday afternoon, early in May, an excited small boy, accompanied by his mother, went up the steps to the front door.

"So this is Pat." Miss Clarice James welcomed her new pupil. She saw a lively, brown-eyed little boy, and her professional eyes noticed his well-proportioned body and strong straight legs. "I'm very pleased to have another boy in my class."

The class was already milling about in the big front room that served as a studio. There were girls of assorted sizes and shapes in colored party dresses and ribbons; a thin sprinkling of boys, scrubbed clean and wearing their best clothes.

Mrs. Kay joined the row of mothers and discarded outdoor clothes on chairs against the wall. Pat put on his new dancing shoes—the traditional black slipper with cross-over elastic.

The class began.

Miss Clarice James was young. It was not long ago that she had been a pupil herself. She wanted her children to enjoy their dancing as much as she had, and enjoy it they did, to a series of lively tunes from the piano.

Beginners were gently initiated into the mysteries of the five positions of the feet in classical ballet. They did their first pliés and battements at the bar, then went on to more exciting free dancing. They were elves and fairies; they were butterflies and birds, and the whole class ended up in a romping polka.

"It was lovely." Pat hopped and skipped all the way home. "I do love dancing," and he went off to find Anthony to teach him the polka.

There was no question of curing him of the idea. Dancing was served up at every meal for days. Saturday afternoons were marked as special, red-letter days.

"Extraordinary!" said Mr. Kay and resigned himself to the idea of having a son who enjoyed dancing.

It didn't take Pat long to discover that Miss James held ballet classes on Wednesdays for more advanced pupils.

"It's such a long time to wait till Saturday," he pleaded with his mother. "Couldn't I go on Wednesdays, too?"

Mrs. Kay went to see Miss James.

"I think it would be an excellent idea," she said. "I've already noticed that your Pat is very promising. He has a good ear for rhythm and a remarkably developed sense of balance. I should be very pleased to have him in my Wednesday class. He will soon catch up with the work."

On Wednesdays Pat met the more serious ballet pupils. To the beginners' pliés and battements were added ronds de jambe, elementary adagio, and allegro.

"What funny looking shoes." He watched some of the older girls changing into blocks for the last part of the class.

"It's for point work," they told him.

"What's that?"

"Dancing on your toes." One of them demonstrated.

"Is that difficult?" Pat was intrigued.

"Yes. You have to practice ever so hard."

"Do it again." Pat watched carefully. "I don't think it's so hard," he said at last. "I think I can do it."

"You can't; not in a soft shoe. You have to have special blocks."

"I'm going to try, anyway," Pat went up on his toes and stayed there.

"Look at that!" The girls clustered around.

"Have you done it before?"

"No." Pat was moving around, getting used to the feel of his toes.

Miss James came over to see this phenomenon.

"You must have real dancer's feet, Pat," she told him. "Very strong. It's most unusual."

"Can I get a pair of block shoes too, and do the exercises with the others?" he wanted to know.

"No." She laughed. "Only girls dance on their points."

This did not deter Pat from practicing on his own to amuse himself.

The summer days lengthened into June—hot, golden days that made the gathering rumors of war seem more unreal than ever. Pat and Anthony made new friends at school, and at the beach, where groups of sun-browned children spent long, happy hours swimming and playing.

Grandfather remembered his promise and Pat became the proud owner of a song-bird in a cage. It could also do one trick—a backward somersault.

"We'll teach it others," the old man had said. "I'll show you." But he never did.

There were suddenly no more Saturday morning parades. Then for a few days the house was hushed and quiet with blinds drawn down, and everyone in black, speaking in whispers, while little birds twittered and hopped around looking in vain for the gentle, gnarled old hands that gave them crumbs.

To Pat and Anthony, Grandfather's death had an unreal quality. He just wasn't there any more. It was difficult to associate the old man sitting up in bed feeding his birds, with the flower-covered mound of earth in the cemetery up on the hill.

"I don't think he minded dying," their mother told them. "He was such an old man, and very, very tired."

Grandfather and his birds quickly faded into the half-dream world of remembered things, like the house at Felpham and the little girl on the beach who danced. Disconnected pictures, some vivid, some blurred, strung haphazardly together, making up the tumbled pattern of childhood's memories.

Meanwhile, the future beckoned, and the immediate future for Pat was Miss James's show.

"I'm giving a show at the end of term," she told Mrs. Kay. "I would so like Pat to take part in it, for I regard him as one of my most promising pupils. Do you think you could let him come for extra practice and rehearsals?"

"I think that will be all right," said Mrs. Kay. "I will have to see what his father says."

"I do hope he will agree."

Mr. Kay now had to resign himself to the idea that not only did his son enjoy dancing, but that he had definite talent for it.

He even accompanied Mrs. Kay and Anthony to the Hove Town Hall to see Pat dance.

"Can't think what people see in this dancing business." He looked at Miss James's little ballet pupils in white and pink tutus, hopping rather nervously around the stage.

"There's Pat," said Anthony loudly.

"Sh!" his mother warned.

"Young devil doesn't even look nervous," remarked Mr. Kay. "Looks as though he's enjoying himself up there, eh, Maude. What do you think?"

But Pat's mother watched her son dance and kept her thoughts to herself.

Before the dancing academy closed for summer vacation Mrs. Kay had a long talk with Miss James, who agreed that it would be well worth while to give Pat more serious training. She suggested her own teachers, Grace and Lily Cone.

"They have a school in London," Miss James explained. "But they come to Brighton twice a week to hold ballet classes. I shall certainly be very sorry to lose Pat, but I realize I can't give him the training he needs in my little classes. There is no doubt that he has a great natural gift for dancing."

So it was quietly arranged that next term Pat should start with the Misses Cone.

The fall, however, was still far away. Now, the summer vacation was upon them. The end of July brought Pat's tenth birthday. It also brought Philip home from school, a strong, grown-up young man of sixteen.

Mrs. Kay was busy packing trunks for they had planned a family vacation on a farm in Berkshire.

"It'll do us all good to get away for a while," Mrs. Kay had decided.

In the sunlit peace of the remote farm in Berkshire, the menacing war clouds receded. Far away in Germany soldiers might be massing on the frontiers, and in London tired, anxious statesmen might be working long hours into the night in a last effort to avert disaster, while servicemen all over the country were hurriedly recalled from leave; but here, in the peaceful heart of Berkshire, the heavy crops ripened to gold in the sun, the air was fragrant with the last of the new hay, gathered on to the ricks, and cattle moved lazily through rich, green fields.

Here, it was easy to push back the haunting specter of war. School, lessons, everything was forgotten but the glory of the moment, as the boys explored their new territory. There were trees to climb, haystacks to slide down, streams to play in, big cart horses to ride, calves and baby pigs to watch, dogs, kittens and chickens and all the exciting freedom of a farm.

But one day, when they came home from a bird-nesting expedition, the boys found a little knot of people gathered at the farmhouse door. A red-faced boy on a bicycle seemed to be the center of attention.

"What is it?" Philip and Pat looked around the circle of serious faces.

"War," said Mr. Kay quietly. "Germany has invaded Belgium, and at midnight we declared war on her." His solemn words struck a cold chill to the heart.

"Yes. I saw it as I was coming through the village." The red-faced boy spoke up. "They were putting up the placards." He had already learned the piece by heart. " 'A state of War exists and mobilization has been ordered.' That's what it says."

"Mobilization." The thud of endless marching boots. Armies on the move. Sounds that made the heart beat faster with mingled fear and excitement. War. The little group of people stood wondering deep in their hearts how this war would touch their lives. It was Philip who voiced the unspoken thought.

"What happens now?" he asked. "What do we do about it?"

There seemed to be no answer to this. They looked at each other, and the slow-voiced farmer at last spoke his mind.

"The way I see it," he said, "war is a job for the professional soldier." He shifted his weight from one foot to the other. "I don't see how it touches us here. War or not, people must have food; cows have to be milked, the harvest got in, and the stock cared for. That's our job and I reckon we go on doing it." This piece of countryman's good sense made everyone feel much better.

"He's quite right," added the farmer's wife, looking at her own sons. "There's nothing any of us here can do, except go on with our work." She looked at Mrs. Kay. "Thank God your boys are not old enough to be needed. So don't you let it spoil their vacation."

It didn't; for Pat and Anthony, still too young to be touched by the shadow of war, drew Philip back into the charmed circle of their own vivid, childhood world, and August, 1914, the last carefree vacation of the whole family together, was to remain for them all a golden, sunlit memory they would treasure all their lives.

6

Charity Show

"READY AT the bar everyone. In the first position for your pliés." The long line of pupils rose and fell to the measure of the music.

"Keep your heels on the ground as you go down. Body straight." Miss Cone came slowly along the line. "Pat, press your knees farther out. . . . Good! Now rest, everybody. Ready for pliés in second position."

There was no fooling around in Miss Cone's class, no more frilly dresses and romping polkas. This was serious ballet with girls in business-like black practice tunics, and boys in plain shirts and shorts.

"How is Pat getting on?" Mrs. Kay asked Miss Cone after the first few lessons.

"He is a very promising pupil," Miss Cone assured her.

"He has quite a natural talent, and if only he will work hard, he should do very well."

"Doesn't he work hard?"

"Not all the time, I'm afraid." Miss Cone smiled. "You see, he wants to dance, now, at once, and sometimes he gets bored with the dull exercises he has to learn. Those are the bad days when I can't make him work at all."

"I am sorry." Mrs. Kay was surprised and disappointed. "I'll talk to him about it."

"I think it would be better to leave him alone." Miss Cone was wise in the ways of artistic children. "If he really has it in him to dance he will do it. It is natural that he should get bored sometimes with the routine work. Do you know what he did the other day to play a joke on me? He got the others to dress him up as a girl and bring him in as a new pupil. There he was in a little tunic, dancing on his points. I had to be cross with him at the time for he was disorganizing the whole class, but how we laughed afterwards, my sister and I."

"The young devil." But Mrs. Kay couldn't help laughing too. "Isn't that just like his mischief?"

"He was very sorry afterwards," Miss Cone went on, "and worked twice as hard to make up for it. I know he really wants to learn and if he has the patience to go through with his training he should make a very fine dancer."

At home, Mr. Kay was more concerned with the war news than with his son's progress at dancing class. In his den, submerged in a deep, leather armchair, he studied newspapers and maps, and grew restive because he was too old to take part in the war.

Philip was too young, or so they all thought, until he suddenly announced that he had signed up.

"Everyone says the fighting will be over in six months," he told them. "I don't want to miss it."

He had given his age as eighteen. He was tall enough to look that much older. The recruiting office believed him, and shortly afterwards, his papers arrived with orders to join a Training Unit, and Pat and Anthony were saying goodby to a grown-up soldier brother.

"I'll be back before long." Philip's courage was high as he left them. "We'll soon finish off those Germans."

"Wish I were going with him," his father said as he watched him go.

"I'm glad you can't. It's enough to lose one of you." Mrs. Kay hugged her two younger sons close to her and thanked God that at least the war couldn't take these from her. How proud she felt of her oldest son, and how afraid for him too.

All over the country, young men like Philip were disappearing from the civilian scene, to be turned into drab, khaki figures with packs on their backs and rifles in their hands.

But while the great machinery of Mobilization slowly gathered speed and strength, everyday life at home went on much as usual. There were still houses to be run, meals to be fixed, shopping to do, school for the children.

Weeks and months went by and the first high hopes that the war would soon be over faded as the armies dug themselves into trenches. Spring came; then summer. Philip arrived home on leave—a tall stranger in khaki who had suddenly become a man. There was no family vacation this summer.

Pat celebrated his eleventh birthday at home. He, too, had grown a lot during the past year and, already, three terms of ballet training had stamped him as a classical dancer, with a compact, well-balanced body, and strong straight legs. Miss Cone soon realized, as she watched his progress, that he was one of her most promising pupils, and it was not long before the opportunity came to test his talent outside the classroom.

One Saturday Pat came home from dancing class bubbling with excitement.

"Miss Cone is giving a show and she wants me to dance in it. It's going to be in a real theatre."

"It's a great honor to have been chosen, darling."

"She told me what she wants me to do." Pat was full of enthusiasm. "It's to be a surprise and a secret, but you must know about it because you'll have to help."

It turned out it was really a Charity Show that Miss Cone was planning; for even dancing students could do their bit for the war. Pat, encouraged by his mother, worked hard for it, going to extra practices and rehearsals. She herself worked hard making his costumes and selling tickets to all her friends.

It was to be at the Hippodrome at Brighton.

"I hope you're coming to see him dance." Mrs. Kay produced tickets for her husband and Anthony. "I shan't be able to sit with you because I have to be backstage to help Pat change."

The theatre was well filled on the great night. Down in the orchestra, Anthony, very proud to be out alone with his father, sat up especially straight and talked loudly about Pat.

Behind the shrouding velvet curtain, backstage was the usual excited confusion, inseparable from a children's charity show. The two Miss Cones hurried to and fro, trying to be everywhere at once, and succeeding.

"Don't wriggle, Pat, or I'll get this lipstick smeared." Mrs. Kay was trying to color up his mouth. "There you are; I've done the outline; now smooth it in yourself."

"It's all right like that." Pat took a quick look in the glass. He saw a pale face with large brown eyes, very bright in the lights, and a vivid mouth. He was already dressed in his first costume, a navy blue and white sailor suit. "Do you think it's time to go down?" He danced about practicing a few steps of his sailor's hornpipe.

"Come here and let me straighten your hair." Mrs. Kay grabbed him and held him still with one hand while she combed his dark hair smooth with the other.

Miss Grace Cone looked in.

"Ready, Pat?"

"Yes, Miss Cone." He ran forward for inspection.

"Is he all right?" Mrs. Kay asked.

"Yes, he looks very nice," she replied. "You'll have plenty of time to come up here and change before your second number." She looked at Pat's costume hanging up on the rack, smiled, and wished him good luck.

"They're starting." Anthony wriggled excitedly in his seat as the house lights faded and the footlights blazed into action.

The heavy curtain swung off the floor, and to the music of the *Nutcracker Suite* on to the stage came a long line of Miss Cone's corps de ballet.

"Aren't they sweet?" The friendly audience welcomed them in. Never mind if some of them were rather wobbly on their points, and others didn't quite keep time; they looked so young and pretty it didn't matter.

"When's Pat coming on?" Anthony whispered loudly as the corps de ballet floated unevenly into the wings.

"Sh!" said Mr. Kay, and they watched two older girls do their pas de deux.

The music changed and a row of little girls in white blouses, pleated navy-blue skirts, and cocky sailor caps, ran on to the stage.

"There's Pat!" Anthony clutched his father's arm.

Out in front of the row of girls ran a saucy sailor boy, and the rhythm of the hornpipe set everyone's feet tapping.

"Good tune that." This was something Mr. Kay could appreciate. "Plenty of life in it."

The rest of the audience liked it too and the dancers went off to a good round of applause.

The show went on, and in the intermission, Mr. Kay bought Anthony a lemonade.

They both laughed over the antics of two comedy dancers. Somebody sang, a little boy recited a poem, and a group of girls in bare feet and white tunics danced a Greek legend.

"Want to see Pat again." Anthony was growing impatient.

"He'll be on soon, I imagine."

"Perhaps this is him." Anthony sat up as the tune changed for the next number. "Oh no!" He sank back. "It's another girl."

To the strains of Mendelssohn's *Spring Song*, a golden-haired little girl came floating in from the wings. Her small, oval face was very serious as, poised on her toes, she danced. The fluffy pink ballet dress stood out in a cloud around her legs.

"Isn't she sweet?" said a lady behind Anthony.

"Very graceful indeed," said another. Mr. Kay and Anthony, however, were not particularly interested in a little girl dancing.

"Do you think Pat will be on next?" Anthony whispered as the *Spring Song* came to an end. The little girl sank down in a low, graceful curtsey before the applause she had won.

"Well done," people called. "Very nice." The clapping faltered. There was a gasp as the little girl rose up again. Her pink ballet frock had fallen to the ground. The golden wig had suddenly vanished, and there was the cropped dark head and thin body of a boy.

"It's Pat!" Anthony suddenly shouted. "Look. It's Pat!"

The audience loved it. Applause and laughter echoed through the theatre, as Pat, clothed only in a pair of pink shorts, picked up his dress, waved his wig at them, grinning mischievously, and went running off into the wings where his mother waited for him.

"A very good show, Pat." Miss Cone came into the dressing-room after the performance was all over. "Our secret was a great success."

There was a knock on the door and a man came in. Miss Cone introduced Mr. Boardman, the manager of the theatre.

"I just looked in to congratulate your boy, Mrs. Kay," he said. "Very good little number he gave tonight. The public loved it. Good idea, dressing him up as a girl."

"I got the idea from Pat himself." Miss Cone smiled at Pat as she re-told the story of the practical joke he had played on her.

"I must say it's the first time I've seen a boy dance on his toes," said Mr. Boardman. "And it comes natural to you?"

"Yes."

"He's been excited about dancing ever since he was a small boy," added Mrs. Kay.

"Does he want to do it professionally?"

"I don't know." She looked at Pat doubtfully.

"He should," said Mr. Boardman. "Your boy has talent, Mrs. Kay. Believe me, I've seen enough youngsters on the stage in my time to recognize the real thing when I see it."

"We've never really taken Pat's dancing very seriously," Mrs. Kay explained. "We only let him go to classes because he was so keen on it, but if he really has talent for this sort of thing . . ."

"There's no question about it." Mr. Boardman was emphatic. "Your boy has a natural gift for the stage. I would strongly advise you to have him trained, and let him make it his career."

"I quite agree with you," added Miss Cone.

"Yes, but how does one go about it?" Mrs. Kay looked from one to the other, sensing that a crossroads had been reached in Pat's life, and that a far-reaching decision would have to be made.

"He needs proper training."

"If I could have him at our school in London," Miss Cone suggested, "he could have full-time training and the chance of work in West End theatres."

"Miss Cone's right." Mr. Boardman nodded his agreement. "I'd say London is the place for him."

Mrs. Kay, faced with this sudden inrush of new ideas, looked to her son for help.

"What do you think about it, Pat?" But even before she asked, she knew what the answer would be. It was shining in his eyes.

"London," he said.

7

London

IT WAS A CLEAR, summer dawn, and two large, snub-nosed furniture vans were chugging purposefully along the road to London. At the back of one, perched among the piled-up furniture, Pat watched the ribbon of road slipping away under the solid rubber tires. Beside him, in a large, open packing case, was his bird-cage. High above the clatter and fuss of the motor, poured the clear notes of a bird's song.

"He's singing for me," said Pat to himself. "He's singing because he's happy we're going to London," and his own heart seemed to rise with happiness to the bird's song. "You'll bring me luck," he said aloud, and at the sound of his voice the bird stopped singing, hopped on to his swinging perch, turned a backward somersault and cocked his head on one side to see if his master was looking.

"Do another," said Pat. The bird swung over again and again; round and round he went, and as Pat watched, he seemed to see his grandfather again, teaching him to do the trick. That made him think of the house at Hove, deserted now, all the rooms empty and unfriendly. He wondered who would go and live there; if anyone would feed the birds in the garden. Then he thought ahead to the new house in London and tried to imagine what it would be like. He wished Anthony was with him. They would have had a wonderful time together in the van, climbing over the furniture and waving to the people as they passed. Poor Anthony was at boarding school this term. Pat remembered the day he had gone off, looking rather self-conscious in his new uniform and school cap, and very determined not to cry.

"Thank goodness they didn't make me go, too," he thought with relief, for boarding school would have meant the end of his ballet; but he knew that his mother understood that dancing had become the most important thing in his life. He thought of his first appearance at the Hippodrome in the pink ballet dress and the golden wig. He remembered too, as he had come on to the stage, how the sudden glare of the footlights had dazzled him so that he had forgotten his steps. He could still hear Miss Cone's urgent whisper from the wings.

"That's right, Pat dear, now do a pas de chat, turn around on your toes, now glissade and ensemble. Repeat dear, that's a good child."

Luckily the audience hadn't seemed to notice anything.

He'd gotten used to the footlights now, for the little girl with golden hair had since made several successful appearances at Charity Shows, as well as the small boy Pat Kay, who danced, and even sang or recited poems that his mother taught him.

"I shall recite you a poem," he shouted at his bird through the vibrating roar of the motors. The bird stopped turning somersaults and listened politely, with his head cocked on one side.

"Did you like it?" Pat inquired. "I like reciting poems, but I'd rather dance." He stretched his legs out on the top of the packing case and looked at his bird through his knees.

"I want to dance." He wriggled his toes about. "I want to dance like those people Miss Cone tells us about." He frowned, trying to remember. "Pavlova. That's right, and Karsavina. They're very famous. And who was the wonderful man who could jump higher than anyone else . . . what was his name . . . Ni . . . Nijinsky. Yes, I'm going to dance as well as he did. Mother and Father keep telling me that if I go on the stage, I ought to be an actor," he confided to his bird. "But I'd much rather dance to lovely music." His bird bobbed about on its perch in agreement, and went spinning around in another series of back somersaults.

Pat yawned suddenly and wondered what time they would arrive, and whether Father and Mother would get there first. They were going by train. He had been allowed, as a great treat, to travel with the furniture. It had meant getting up at half-past four, a horrible, cold, middle-of-the-night feeling, dragging oneself, half asleep out of a warm bed to stand shivering in the chill, gray morning air, pulling on one's clothes, and feeling slightly sick. A welcome, scalding hot cup of tea, and by five o'clock they had been on the move. The big vans had gone rumbling through the deserted streets, past the quiet, sleeping houses. A last glimpse of the sea, a misty blue-gray line beyond the roofs and chimneys, and they were out of the town, and away in the open country. The sun had come up, turning the sky to blue and gold with all the promise of a glorious summer day, and the long ribbon of road stretched ahead of them.

He wondered what time it was now. It seemed they had been traveling for hours and hours. They had stopped three times on the road already, to put water into the motors and tea into the men. Pat felt sleepy but it was too bumpy to do anything about it, for every time he laid his head on something it got jolted off again, so he sang songs to his bird, or watched the road, and the throbbing motor shook him into a dazed, half-awake state.

One more stop before the spreading tentacles of the London suburbs reached out to them, and soon the open fields and gardens were crowded out, as the miles of grimy brick closed in. How did anyone find his way about this tangle of streets, Pat wondered. They all looked alike, a squalid, dingy muddle of cobbles and trolley tracks, factory walls, sooty houses, and rows of huddled shops.

Then, quite suddenly, they had come out of the clanking traffic and the crowds that swarmed through the sprawling, brick wilderness of south London; they were on an open bridge, with the wide, brown Thames shining below.

A few more twists and turns and the vans came to a stop.

"Well, sonny, here we are." One of the men came around to lift him down. "Safe and sound at your new home."

Pat stood on the pavement and looked up at 49 Bishops Mansions, Fulham.

The front door was open and the men from the first van were already carrying in the furniture.

"Aren't you going in to look at your new home?" one of them asked. Pat shook his head. The house suddenly didn't interest him. He wanted to be away, on his own. He turned and wandered along to the end of the road, where he found the park that fringed the bank of the Thames. In the far corner was a railing. Here he sat, a small, solitary figure, looking down at the wide, shining river sliding past.

"I'm in London," he said softly to himself. "We've come to live in London, and all because of me."

He looked along to the strings of barges moored out in the stream. He saw the distant huddle of wharves, and beyond them the crowded, smoky skyline that held the pulsing heart of the capital. London was to be his home. A new life was beginning, like a new chapter waiting to be written. What did the future hold for him?

He looked up. Overhead, slow, white clouds drifted over the smoky gray pall of the city. He watched them, his mind crowded with dreams and half-formed ambitions; but through them all beat the steady determination to make his own way in life, to do something that mattered, to be someone who counted in this great city.

London seemed to fling out a challenge. He accepted it.

8
The First Job

"DEAR ANTHONY . . ." Pat, kneeling on a chair, sprawled over the table, pen in hand. "It's been very dull since you went back to school . . ."

He stared at the rest of the blank page in front of him thinking over the summer vacation. It had been fun having Anthony home, showing him the new house, and exploring London. They had enjoyed being together, but they had both missed the old, free life with the garden and the sea. It wasn't really much fun being in London in August when the hot, sunny days made one long to go running down to the beach for a swim.

Though neither of them had said much about it, they had missed Philip badly.

"Philip thinks he'll be coming home on leave soon," he wrote. "I hope it'll be in the Christmas holidays; then you'll see him too . . . "

How lovely it would be for the three of them to be together.

Pat felt very alone now that Anthony had gone back to his boarding school.

". . . I hope you have a good term. . . ." He chewed the end of his pen thoughtfully and a blob of ink fell on to the page. "I go to dancing classes every day at Miss Cone's. I love it. I have a governess now, Miss Etwell. She has red hair and very long eyelashes. I thought she stuck them on but I looked through the keyhole and she doesn't . . . "

He looked over his shoulder as the door opened, and there was Miss Etwell coming into the schoolroom. She was slim and pale, in a white blouse, a long black skirt, with a broad, shiny black belt pulled very tightly around her waist. She frowned as she saw the sprawling figure of her pupil.

"Pat, what are you doing?"

"I'm writing a letter." He looked at her out of the corner of his eyes, wondering if she could see what he'd written.

"Sit down on the chair properly," she told him.

"I write better like this."

"Nonsense," she insisted. "Sit down."

"She's just come in . . . " Pat's spidery writing went on, as he reluctantly got into the required position. The letter was hurriedly finished.

"Have you learned your poem yet?" Miss Etwell settled herself in the big armchair and picked up the paper. "Your mother wants to go over it with you this evening."

Miss Cone's Charity Shows were still with them.

"I know most of it." Pat sighed, picked the book out of the untidy pile on the table, twisted himself into a new knot on the chair, and began to study.

The silence in the schoolroom was broken only by the crackle and fall of the coals in the fire and the rustle of Miss Etwell's paper. Pat fidgeted uneasily, muttering his poem to himself, while Miss Etwell read through the war news. No signs of peace yet in this daily record of battle and death. The war had been going on for over two years now.

Miss Etwell sighed, and turned over the page in search of something that made more cheerful reading. A little paragraph caught her eye.

"Oh!" she exclaimed. "There's something here that might interest you, Pat. Boys and girls are wanted to take part in a play."

"Let's see?" Pat came and looked over her shoulder. " 'Auditions will be held for a forthcoming production by Mr. Seymour Hicks,' " he read out. "Who's that?"

"Haven't you heard of Mr. Hicks? He's a very famous actor."

"I wonder what sort of a play it is." Pat's interest was aroused.

"The auditions are on October 28th." Miss Etwell looked at the advertisement again. "That's the day after tomorrow. At the Prince's Theatre."

"I don't see why I shouldn't try for that. I'll show this to Mother and see what she thinks." Pat went running off to find her.

Outside the Prince's Theatre, a lugubrious commissionaire, with a white mustache, was standing on guard.

"Brought your little boy for the audition, lady?" He gazed mournfully at Mrs. Kay. "Not in here. Round the back." He jerked a thumb. "Stage door."

"Audition, lady?" The stage door keeper glared at them disapprovingly. "Through that door there."

Pat and his mother found themselves on a stage, bare of scenery, and swarming with people.

"Do you think they've all come for the audition?" Pat gazed at this alarming, churning crowd of girls and boys.

A harassed looking stage manager, trying to make his way through, was besieged.

"What time does it begin?" One mother pulled at his sleeve.

"Where can I change my little girl's dress?" Another closed in, plucking at his coat.

"Where is the pianist?" A third waved a sheaf of music under his nose. "I want him to go over my little boy's song."

"Will we have to wait long?"

"I don't know." The stage manager looked desperate and fled.

Mrs. Kay drew Pat aside.

"We'll just stand here and wait until they tell us where to go."

"Is Mr. Hicks here?" Pat wanted to know.

"He's over there." A nearby mother overheard them. She pointed.

Pat standing on tiptoe, caught sight of two men surrounded by a swirling tide of mothers.

"That one on the left is Mr. Hicks," he was told. "The dark man with him is Mr. Wolheim, his manager."

"What play is it?" asked Mrs. Kay.

"It's a revival of *Bluebell in Fairyland.* It's several years now since Mr. Hicks has done it. Lovely play for the kiddies. He wrote it himself, you know."

Someone clapped his hands.

"Clear the stage, please."

Parents and children were herded into the side. Mr. Hicks and Mr. Wolheim made their way down to some seats in front.

The audition began.

One by one the children were called out to do their pieces. Some recited, some sang, others danced. Pat's mother had made him prepare two or three of the recitations he had done at Charity Shows.

"Which shall I do?" he whispered urgently as the boys were called out and it began to look like his turn soon.

She didn't answer, for she was watching a mournful looking boy on the stage plodding his way through a mournful poem.

"That will do, sonny." Mr. Hicks interrupted him after two verses. "You can go." He turned to Mr. Wolheim beside him and Mrs. Kay overheard him say: "No good, too sentimental."

"Next, please."

The stage manager looked over the line of boys.

"Your turn," he signed to Pat.

Mrs. Kay bent and whispered quickly:

"Recite 'Dan Cupid.' "

Mr. Hicks looked up as Pat walked on to the stage. "What's your name, sonny?"

"Pat, sir. Pat Kay."

How old are you?"

"Twelve, sir."

"Done any stage work before?"

"Yes, sir." He hoped he wouldn't be asked for details.

"What are you going to do now?"

"Recite a poem."

"All right. Go ahead." Mr. Hicks smothered a yawn.

" 'Dan Cupid,' " Pat announced. The poem was short. It was comic. There was a pause.

"All right, sonny," Mr. Hicks told him. "Go and stand over there, will you, and wait."

Mr. Wolheim, who was taking notes, leaned over and said something.

"Well at least he speaks the King's English," replied Mr. Hicks loudly.

Pat's hopes rose as he crossed to the other side of the stage to join the lucky ones who had also been told to wait. He caught his mother's eye and winked at her.

The audition went on, it seemed, for hours. Gradually the crowd thinned out as the unsuccessful were packed into hats and coats and taken away.

"Is that all?" Mr. Hicks called out at last.

"Yes, sir." The stage manager bobbed into sight.

"Bring these others on." He waved towards the survivors. There were about forty of them in all. They were brought on stage again, lined up, and looked over. Two or three more were sent home. Finally the chosen bunch were paraded into the orchestra. They lined up in the center aisle.

They moved slowly along to Mr. Wolheim who was taking names and addresses.

It was the turn of the small boy in front of Pat.

"The part of the Fish Boy," they heard Mr. Wolheim say. "What salary do you want?"

Pat nudged his mother urgently. "What do we say?"

"I don't know." They looked at each other doubtfully, wondering what on earth one should be paid for a job on the stage. Then, Mrs. Kay heard the "Fish Boy's" father ask for £2.*

"We'll ask for the same," she whispered.

"Pat Kay, 49 Bishops Mansions," Mr. Wolheim wrote it down. "For the part of Peter the Black Cat, £2. There will be twelve performances a week," he told them. "We'll send you the contract. First rehearsal Monday, 10 o'clock."

Pat and his mother were walking on air as they left the theatre. A contract for a West End theatre. How important it sounded. Two pounds a week when one was only twelve years old.

"I'm rich," said Pat.

On the way home he thought of all the things he would buy for the family with his new fortune.

The first rehearsal saw a collection of thirty children and a sprinkling of adults assembled on the stage in front of Mr. Hicks. Mothers were banished into dark corners out of sight. Someone handed out scripts. Mr. Hicks explained what the play was about, and Pat discovered that Peter the Black Cat was quite a leading part, most of it with Bluebell herself.

"Who is playing Bluebell?" he whispered to a big boy standing near him.

"Miss Terriss of course; she always plays it."

"Who's she?"

The boy stared down at him, wondering where this ignorant new arrival had sprung from.

---

*About $6.

"Mr. Hicks's wife, of course. She's over there talking to the stage manager."

Pat had a quick glimpse of a beautiful expressive face.

"We will walk through Act I with books this morning," Mr. Hicks was saying. "The rest of you Fairyland people who aren't in Act I go now with Mr. Farren to learn your dances."

The stage was rapidly cleared. Only a few of them remained. Miss Terriss, self-possessed and charming, came over to where Pat stood by himself, feeling rather lost.

"I hear you are to be my cat, Peter." She smiled at him.

"Yes." Pat looked up at her and thought how lovely she was.

"Is this your first show?"

"Yes, it is really." He felt one didn't mention Charity Shows when one was in a real professional West End theatre.

She looked across to where her husband was talking to some of the men from the cast.

"Come over here in a corner," she whispered. "I'll explain what you have to do before they start."

The rehearsal trailed through the long hours of the morning.

"All right. Break for lunch. Back at 2:30 this afternoon. We'll go through the same act." Mr. Hicks dismissed them.

"Isn't Miss Terriss a wonderful person?" said Pat enthusiastically as he joined his mother.

"I was asking Mr. Wolheim what happened about your school lessons." Mrs. Kay, at that moment, was more concerned with Pat's education. "We can't have you missing your school work every day like this. He tells me they hire a governess to teach all you children here, on the spot, so that they can fit in school with the rehearsals."

Pat, however, thinking about the beautiful Miss Terriss, wasn't listening, and Mrs. Kay went on talking to herself.

"I wonder if Miss Etwell would be interested in applying for the job."

Miss Etwell was. She applied; Mrs. Kay recommended her highly to Mr. Wolheim, and she got the job. What a job too!

In a makeshift schoolroom in an office building opposite the theatre, she faced, each day, her unruly class of thirty rowdy, high-spirited boys and girls.

The rehearsals dragged on. Through tears and temperaments, curses and praise, boredom and delight, Bluebell and her fairy world were slowly and painfully brought to life.

There were the days when things went well and Mr. Hicks was charming.

There were the other days.

"No! You little fool." Mr. Hicks raged at Pat. "Think what you're doing. My God, the boy's got no brains." And Pat, paralyzed with fright, had none.

"Go through that bit again, and remember, in this second act you're no longer just an animal, you've become human."

How complicated it was, to be a cat and a human at the same time.

"Not so fast," Mr. Hicks screamed from the stalls. "Watch your timing. Now, go back and take it again."

Pat, near to tears, took it again.

"All right, go on."

"Don't worry, Peter, dear, you're all right," Miss Terriss whispered to him. "It's coming on well." Pat adored her.

At the end of the rehearsal Mr. Hicks called him over.

"Yes, sir." Pat ran across the stage wondering what fresh horrors lay in store.

"Here, sonny, catch!" A coin flicked across the footlights, a silver half-crown landed in Pat's hand.

"Go and buy yourself a box of chocolates." Mr. Hicks, without waiting for Pat's startled and incoherent thanks, turned away to talk to someone else.

Pat looked up from the half-crown and saw Miss Terriss smiling at him.

"Do you think it's all right to take it?" he asked anxiously.

"Of course, take it, Peter." She always called him by his part name. "Take anything you can get."

"But I worked so badly today. I mean, Mr. Hicks was so annoyed with me."

"That's his way of showing you that it's all forgotten." She came and put her arm around him. "You mustn't let it worry you so much, when he gets cross. You see, he gets impatient. We've done Bluebell so many times before that he knows exactly how he wants each bit played, and you can't always manage it the first time, or even the second time. After all, you're very young and you just haven't had the experience, but he forgets that. I know it seems very hard, but you take my advice." She leaned closer to him. "Try not to mind about the shouting, but take notice of all these things he tells you. You can learn such a lot from him."

Her gentle words poured healing into Pat's sore heart, giving him back his confidence in himself.

He smiled up at her, finding no words to express the swelling gratitude for her understanding and encouragement.

His day, however, was not finished. Mr. Farren had still to have the last word.

"Rehearsal Act II, same time tomorrow." The stage manager came on. "Will those of you who dance in Act I stay behind, please. Mr. Farren wants to run through the dances now."

The children involved looked at each other and sighed. Dance rehearsals provoked nearly as many storms as the others.

"Peter, on stage, please," Mr. Farren called Pat out. "We'll go through your minuet. Can you remember the steps from last time?"

"I think so." Pat had done it once only.

The music started.

"No." Mr. Farren stopped him. "Two paces to the right bow, and then turn to the left."

Pat tried again and didn't seem able to get the hang of it.

"No," Mr. Farren came on stage. "Follow me now. Do it like this. One, two–bow, and turn to the left." He demonstrated.

Pat, tired and flustered from the storm of his other rehearsal with Mr. Hicks, took two paces, bowed and turned to the right.

Mr. Farren's blood pressure rose.

"Left, I said, not right," he shouted.

A bored pianist in the wings thumped out the bars again. Pat, panic stricken, forgot his bow.

That finished it.

"Leave it alone." Mr. Farren strode off the stage in a fury. "You may make an actor, my lad," he shouted for all the world to hear, "but my God, you'll never be a dancer."

Pat felt he had now heard everything.

9

Peter the Black Cat

"HERE'S YOUR costume, duckie." The wardrobe mistress brought the black cat's skin into the dressing-room and hung it on the rack. "I want to see you in it before you go on."

"Yes," said Pat.

"Now where's the Fish Boy? I want you during the intermission."

The door opened and Mr. McKay, one of the men in the cast, looked in.

"Is Peter the Cat in here?"

"Yes." Pat, half undressed, twisted around on his chair.

"I've been told to come and make you up." Mr. McKay did not appear to relish the idea.

"Do I finish getting changed first?"

"No. Always make up before you put on your costume." Mr. McKay was young, tall, and elegant and obviously had no time for little boys.

Pat presented his face and Mr. McKay ungraciously covered it with an assortment of colors.

"Can't think why they don't teach you little beggars to make yourselves up before you start on this profession." He squinted down a greasepaint stick at Pat's eyebrows, and went on grumbling as he worked.

"Well, there you are. That'll have to do." He gave a final dab of powder. "It's a straight make-up. I suppose that's what they want."

"Thank you very much."

Pat turned and looked at himself in the glass. At least, he supposed it was himself, for an entirely strange object was staring back at him. He saw a startling pink face, two black eyes, a red and rather shapeless mouth and two heavy black eyebrows.

Mr. McKay had gone.

Pat turned to his neighbor, the Fish Boy and asked, "Am I supposed to look like this, do you think?"

The Fish Boy gazed at him without flinching.

"I guess it'll be all right in the lights," he said.

Pat got into his costume. The cat's skin was all in one piece, buttoning up the front. He had big, padded paws at the end of his arms and legs, and a molded cat's head which left just a hole under the jaw, where his face appeared.

The call-boy rapped on the door.

"Overture and beginners please," he called in his sing-song voice. They went trooping down the stairs to the stage.

Miss Terriss, a radiant-looking Bluebell, was standing in the wings, as calm and untroubled as always.

"How's my Peter feeling?" She smiled at Pat, and whatever she thought of Mr. McKay's efforts on his face, she tactfully gave no sign.

"I'm all right, thank you, Miss Terriss." He thought how young and lovely she looked. She didn't seem to have any make-up on at all.

"Not nervous?" she asked him.

"No." He shook his head. It had never occurred to him to be nervous. Looking at her face more carefully he could see now how she had put on her make-up. He noticed the careful eye shadow, and the rouge of her cheeks that blended into the deepened color of her skin. Pat resolved to make up his own face next time.

"Is your mother out in front tonight?"

"Yes, and my father too."

Mr. Hicks came toward them. He was tense with nerves.

"Ah! There you are, Ellaline." His presence charged the atmosphere with electricity. "You won't forget that new business in the second scene? You! Peter . . ." He jabbed a finger at Pat. "Don't hurry that minuet . . ." He broke off as he noticed Pat's face. "Good God, what a make-up. Get someone to show you how to do it next time. . . . Oh, Eric!" He caught sight of Mr. Wolheim, and went charging off before Pat could explain about his face; not that Mr. Hicks would have listened anyway.

"Why is he so nervous?" Pat wanted to know. "I mean he's been on the stage before so he ought to be used to it."

Miss Terriss laughed.

"Lucky boy," she told him. "You don't know yet about first-night nerves."

"But you're not nervous."

"It's very sweet of you to say so. You see," she confided to him, "I am really, inside of me, but I try not to let it show. It's enough to have one in the family with nerves!"

The stage manager came by.

"Ready, Miss Terriss?"

"Yes." Her hand rested a moment on Pat's arm. "Good luck, Peter."

To Pat, all this first-night business had a strangely unreal quality, like a game of make-believe at a party. In spite of rehearsals, or perhaps because of them, he still had only the most confused idea of what the whole play was all about. He thought of his own part as merely a string of things to be said and actions to be done, exactly as Mr. Hicks had taught him, without in the least understanding why.

Meanwhile, the curtain was up. The play had begun.

"Ready for your cue, Peter?" Someone whispered to him in the darkness of the wings.

"Yes, I'm ready." He crouched down on all fours, close to the window, timing his entrance. This was it—now!

The Black Cat jumped through the window and on to the bed, just as he had learned to do at rehearsals.

"Don't hurry it." He could almost hear Mr. Hicks's voice beside him. "Stay on the bed a moment. Give the audience a chance to see you before you jump down and cross to Bluebell." Automatically Pat carried out his instruction. He crouched on the bed looking around, but, as he paused there, he suddenly realized that it wasn't his imagination. He could really hear Mr. Hicks's voice. An angry, hissing whisper was coming from the wings, and it was directed at him. What was he doing wrong this time? He jumped hastily off the bed, and in the panic of the moment, got up on his hind legs and walked across to Bluebell on two feet instead of four paws.

The vicious whispering was plainly audible now.

"Get down on all fours, you little fool." The full force of Mr. Hicks's rage hit him. "Don't show your face to the audience. What do you think you are doing?"

Poor Peter. The magic and excitement had fled, and a terrified small boy dropped on to his hands and knees. His mouth opened and a sad, pitiful "Miaow" came from his choked-up throat. Thank goodness he had managed to get that sound out in the right place.

This was Bluebell's cue to turn around and see her cat—a cat who was vowing to himself at that moment that nothing would induce him ever to go on the stage again. Then he saw Bluebell's face. She gave him a special look and a smile. He came and rubbed his head against her, stroking her dress with one paw. The audience loved it, and the Cat decided that the stage wasn't so bad after all.

The rest of Bluebell's first night went without a hitch.

After the show was all over his mother and father came around to the dressing-room.

"It was wonderful, darling." His mother hugged him.

"Very good, my boy." Mr. Kay, tall, slim and sporting, looked quite out of place among the clutter of the boys' dressing-room.

"Did you see when I went wrong at the beginning?" Pat, still worked up, found relief in talking. "Mr. Hicks shouted at me from the wings; it was awful."

"I didn't notice anything," his mother said reassuriedly.

"You must have. I walked across the stage instead of going on all fours."

"Oh that!" she said easily. "Nobody would notice, or if they did they wouldn't remember."

"The whole thing looked all right to me," said his father. "Very good play. Fine actor, Mr. Hicks."

"What a charming Bluebell Miss Terriss is," said Mrs. Kay. "I thought it was altogether a beautiful production."

The first night was over. The revived Bluebell was welcomed back into theatreland. Box office business was good. Mr. Hicks was charming and everyone breathed more easily.

Bluebell settled down to her task of taking two audiences a day into the charmed world of fairyland that waited behind the big velvet curtains.

For the children in the cast, the run of Bluebell was one long frolic, starting in the morning when the whole, rowdy, romping crowd of them collected in the classroom with one idea only in mind—to have as much fun and as little school as possible.

By lunch time Miss Etwell may have been worn out, but not her lively charges. Fortified with sandwiches, cake, and milk they swarmed happily into the theatre to get ready for the matinee, and invaded the dressing-rooms with noise, laughter, and practical jokes, most of which were attributed to Pat.

At intervals an outraged stage manager read the riot act and threatened to have them put out of the show.

"But I didn't mean to drop it on the stage." Pat, full of virtuous indignation stood before the stage manager. "It was a mistake."

The subject of dispute was a stink bomb that had made hideous the whole of the first act.

"Oh! And where did you mean to drop it, may I inquire?"

"In the girls' dressing-room."

"You did, did you?" And the stage manager, suddenly seeing again the faces of the cast as they had acted their way through a stench of sulphurous decay, had to turn away quickly to hide a laugh.

The stink bomb incident was followed by the ink episode.

"No, I didn't put ink on the other children's clothes." Pat defended himself hotly against the wardrobe mistress's accusations. It was quite true that he hadn't, but he got blamed for it anyway. How unjust!

Slightly less unjust was the rage of one of the actors, Fred Buckstone, who came storming into the boys' dressing-room, his eyes red and streaming.

"Which of you has been messing with my mustache? You . . ." he caught sight of Pat. "I suppose it's . . . Ah! . . . Ah! Ahtishoo!" A mighty sneeze shook him from top to toe. There was a riotous giggle from the boys.

"You—just wait till I get hold of you . . ." Another sneeze shook him.

Pat didn't wait. He fled to hide in the wings, where a delighted bunch of children gathered to watch poor Fred Buckstone struggle through his part fighting the itching, tickling sneezing powder that Pat had thoughtfully sprinkled in his mustache.

So it went on. Bluebell ran for three happy months at the Prince's Theatre, and all too soon came the sad day in March when they gave the last performance and were saying goodby.

"See you next year," they all said to each other, for surely there would be another Bluebell next Christmas time.

"What are you going to do after this?" one of them asked Pat.

"I don't know." He shrugged his shoulders. "Ordinary lessons again I suppose." How dull and flat it would be, he thought. Lessons by himself again with Miss Etwell.

It didn't work out that way, however, for at home his father was to ask the same question.

"What are we going to do with Pat now this is over?"

"Nothing, dear." Mrs. Kay was surprised. "I mean he'll

go on with his dancing and school lessons as before, won't he?"

Mr. Kay, however, had been doing some serious thinking.

"It's all very well, this acting business, but the boy has to have a proper education," he announced.

"He gets a proper education from Miss Etwell," said Mrs. Kay mildly. "I'm sure she's very good with him."

"A boy of his age needs a man to teach him and proper school discipline." Mr. Kay spoke very firmly. "He's been running wild these last months, and hasn't learned a thing. I tell you, Maude, the boy should go to a boarding school like his brothers."

They had had discussions like this before, but Mrs. Kay realized that this time her husband really meant business. He was deeply concerned over Pat's lack of what he called proper education.

"What about his dancing lessons if he goes away to school?"

"Look here, Maude, you're not going to spoil the boy's chances for the future because of this idea that he likes dancing." Mr. Kay spoke with great decision. "After all, he's only twelve, we don't know if he's going to be any good on the stage when he grows up. We've got to give him a decent education to fit him to earn his own living."

Mrs. Kay had, unwillingly, to admit that his reasoning was perfectly right. Pat should have a proper schooling. Why then did all her instincts cry out against making this drastic change in his life?

"We've sent Philip to a good school, and Anthony too. We'll do the same for Pat," said Mr. Kay, and she knew her cause was lost.

"Will you send him to the same school as Anthony?" she asked him.

"No," he replied. "Anthony has settled down very nicely on his own. We don't want Pat to arrive and lead him into mischief. We'll find another place." He was determined to have his own way, and he got it.

So it came about that, at the beginning of the term, a cross and miserable Pat was put into a uniform and dispatched to a boarding school.

10

"A Proper Education"

"I HATE IT HERE; when can I leave?" Pat wrote with unfailing regularity to his parents, and his mother wrote back with equal regularity, but without conviction.

"You must be patient. I'm sure you'll like it when you've gotten used to it."

A half-term report informed them that Pat's progress in education was practically nil, whereas his performance at games and sports was remarkable.

"Looks as though he'll turn into a fine sportsman," Mr. Kay read this part of the report with high approval. "Much better life for a boy, proper healthy outdoor activities."

"I thought you sent him away to be well educated," suggested Mrs. Kay with gentle malice. "His school work doesn't seem to be advancing much."

Mr. Kay's reply was inarticulate.

"We had the school sports on Saturday," Pat wrote later on in the term. "I won two races and got the silver cup for high jump, 2nd prize for long jump, and 1st prize for gym. I like gym. I'm learning to walk on my hands, and I can do somersaults in the air off the springboard."

Mr. Kay, who was reading the letter, looked up.

"Fine show, Maude, winning all those prizes." He was very proud of his son's achievements.

He was less pleased, however, with the rest of the letter.

"Only eighteen more days to the end of term," it went on. "Can I have dancing lessons during vacation? I do miss them here."

"Dancing lessons!" his father snorted. "What is this nonsense? I thought he'd forget all about that business. Can't understand the boy at all."

Poor Mr. Kay, puzzled and hurt that his son, who showed all the promise of being a fine athlete and sportsman, should still cling to this absurd idea that he wanted to dance.

"If he was no good at anything else, Maude, I'd understand it." He shook his head. "But for a boy who gets prizes . . . " He appealed to her, and Mrs. Kay, who loved and knew them both so well, realized that he never would understand the wild, Irish spirit that Pat had inherited from her. He never would be in sympathy with this strange urge to dance.

"I can't explain it," she said. "I think it is just one of the things about Pat that we must accept without understanding."

"Thank goodness we don't get this trouble from Anthony." Mr. Kay tossed the letter aside.

Mrs. Kay smiled, said nothing, and quietly went off to

see whether Miss Cone could give Pat dancing lessons during August.

The end of July brought Pat home: a thinner, taller, quieter Pat. A couple of days later, Anthony, released from his establishment, arrived back; a very self-possessed schoolboy now, of a year's standing.

Pat's quietness wore off rapidly, and the house echoed to rowdy, schoolboy noises. Pat set out his sports prizes on the mantelpiece and turned the bedroom into a gymnasium, where he and Anthony tried out doubtful and highly dangerous experiments in acrobatics. In these, Pat found a slight consolation for his lost dancing.

"Do be careful, Pat dear." Their mother looked in, in the middle of one of these sessions. "Anthony! Watch your feet on the wash-stand. Don't break the basin!"

"Mother, you must watch this. It's a new one." Pat climbed on to a chair at the foot of the bed, grasped the bedrail and carefully did a handstand.

"That's very clever." She was genuinely amazed at his skill and control. "What else can you do?" She sat down and watched him, wondering again at his unerring sense of balance.

He came wriggling up beside her. "Mother, if I get a bad school report, do you think Father will let me leave?"

"We'll have to see." She pushed back his dark hair. "Do you think it will be bad?"

"Oh yes!" he replied cheerfully. "I didn't learn a thing, and I was always being punished for fooling around in class. Do you think there's any chance of having dancing lessons during vacation?"

"I went to see Miss Cone, and she told me she was very

sorry she couldn't have you because the school is closed during August."

"Shall we go away to the beach this year?" Anthony wriggled up on the other side.

"No dear, I'm afraid not. It's too difficult with the war; besides, we can't really afford it. You see everything is getting so expensive nowadays, we have to be careful about spending when prices are going up all the time."

"I'll earn lots of money and make you rich, Mother," Pat promised her. "Do you think I'll get a part in Bluebell again at Christmas? Oh!" The brightness had suddenly gone from his eyes. "I'd forgotten school. Please, Mother, you won't keep me there, not while Bluebell is on? I couldn't bear it. I think I should run away, I really would. If you knew how I hated it you wouldn't make me go back."

"I think I do know, darling." She held him close to her, and she knew also by the look on his face when he spoke of school that something would have to be done. She must get him away somehow. "Let's forget all about it for now, shall we?" She chased away the nightmare for him. "I really came in to tell you something nice."

"What is it?"

"A visit to the theatre. Miss Cone said that I was to be sure and take you to the Ballet to see Astafieva. She is dancing at the Coliseum with the Swinburne Ballet."

"Oh!" Pat's eyes lighted again. "Who's Asta . . . whatever you said?"

"Astafieva." She smiled. "Well, I must confess I didn't know, but Miss Cone tells me she is a very fine Russian dancer. Apparently she has a school of her own here, in London, and it's not often she actually appears herself on the stage. Miss Cone says you really mustn't miss it. Would you like to go?"

There was no need to ask. Theatre and Ballet were magic words that spelled music, beauty, and movement, and sent his blood racing. All the old urge to dance, that school life had forced into the background, came flooding up again in full force.

"Let's go soon."

They did.

A few nights later, an excited boy sat beside his mother in the Coliseum waiting for the curtain to go up. To Pat this was like coming back into the world again after long exile. His whole being responded to the sights and sounds around him: the gilt, the plush, the lights, the shuffling crowds filling the house, the buzz of voices, the orchestra tuning up. School life faded into a dim, gray background, and he felt alive all over.

"Serafina Astafieva." Her name made a bit more sense now that he saw it on the printed program in front of him. "Did you say she was Russian?"

"Yes, darling. Miss Cone was telling me that she was trained at the Imperial Ballet School in St. Petersburg."

"And she's got a ballet school of her own here?"

"Yes, she has a studio somewhere in Chelsea. Apparently she is a wonderful teacher as well as being a very fine dancer herself. Miss Cone says she was dancing with Diaghileff's Ballet Russe before she came to London."

"Who's Diaghileff?" Pat asked, but there was no time to know the answer—then. The lights dimmed and the buzz of talk faded into silence.

The curtain rose.

To Pat's young and uncritical eyes, ballet was a world of

enchantment that lifted him out of himself like the soaring flight of a bird.

Tonight as the ballet began he had a dreamlike impression of floating white dancers, grouped like some quivering flower, to be suddenly blown by a gust of music that scattered the white petals and laid bare the living heart: a single, delicate figure, poised on her toes. No need to ask who this was. With Astafieva, a living force had come on to the stage. No dreamlike impression here. Pat sat up, sharply aware of her. She commanded and held his whole attention. Here was a personality as well as a dancer. There was fire in her movements. The sparkle of a pirouette, the flash of a grand jeté, the scintillating brilliance of a string of fouettés, seemed to light up the stage. She clothed the music with shimmering movement, and beside her the others paled to insignificance, at least, to the young boy who sat, still and tense, in the darkness, the color drained from his face, and his eyes, large and brilliant, fixed on that one dancing figure.

He was seeing for the first time the beauty and strength of pure classical dancing. It was a revelation. The perfect control that creates the flawless curve of an arabesque, the clean-cut precision of an entrechat. The style and polish that come only from years of training glittered through every movement.

It was over. The clatter of applause broke up the enchantment, letting in reality. Pat was filled with an unbearable excitement. As surely as if someone had spoken it aloud, he knew now where his own road lay. He turned to his mother.

"I want to learn to dance like that," he told her. "I will, I must learn to dance at Astafieva's school."

If Mrs. Kay hoped that this new idea was a passing fancy, she was wrong. The impression Astafieva had made had gone too deep ever to be forgotten.

"It's no good, dear," Mrs. Kay said, as she came into her husband's study a week or two later. "I've done everything I can to persuade him to give up this idea, and it's impossible. Since he has seen Astafieva he is absolutely convinced that he wants to leave school and study under her. He pesters me all day about it."

"I gave him a good talking to in here." Mr. Kay leaned against the mantelpiece and put his hands in his pockets. "He's a wilful young devil."

"I really think it would do him a lot of harm to force him to go on at boarding school." Mrs. Kay sat sidesaddle on the arm of a chair. "You know yourself, dear, how it is when you are training a spirited young horse. You can bend him so far to your will, but there comes a moment when you have to let him have his head. I believe Pat really would do something desperate if we sent him back to that school."

"Too damned independent for his age." Mr. Kay stared at the carpet as though hoping to find a solution there.

"He has shown us that this wanting to dance isn't just a passing fancy," Mrs. Kay persisted. "After all, it's nearly three years now since he started, and he's keener than ever, and everyone who has taught him says he is unusually promising."

"M'm," Mr. Kay admitted. "The boy certainly knows what he wants and sticks to it. I'll say that for him."

There was a long silence. Slowly, he looked around his study. He was seeing the photos on the walls, cricket groups, pictures of his favorite horses, the case of silver cups he had won at school for sporting events, hunting horns, foxes' masks: treasures that evoked for him the scent and sound of summer days, of cricket matches and tennis, or winter, and long, hard days riding to hounds. These were the good things of life, the things he had enjoyed himself and wanted his sons to enjoy in their turn. But his simple ideas for them weren't working out. First the war had come and taken Philip away into the army. Now Pat was in revolt against boarding school, and all because of this hare-brained idea that he wanted to learn to dance.

Mr. Kay shook his head wearily, remembering Pat's tears and entreaties, and his passionate rages when he was refused, and Maude sided with the boy, seemed to understand him. Well, he had forced his will on them both and sent Pat to school. He'd been so sure the boy would settle down and like it, but he hadn't. Perhaps he needed longer to get used to the idea of school. Perhaps he never would get used to it. Mr. Kay sighed heavily. It was all very difficult.

"In my day, all boys went away to school," he said slowly, "and that was the end of it."

"I think our Pat is different from other boys," said Mrs. Kay softly. "He has this artistic streak in him. I think we should be wise to let him follow his own instincts over this."

"He's got your Irish blood in him, you mean." Mr. Kay looked at her. "You understand him, Maude, and I don't." He straightened his shoulders, and looked away, out of the window.

It was not easy for him to admit he was wrong, that school was a failure. He was a sportsman, though, who knew how to take a defeat, however bitter the disappointment might be. He looked again at his wife.

"There is one thing I insist on," he said. "No more gov-

ernesses. If he leaves school, he must go to a good tutor."
She stood up close to him.

"I don't think you will ever regret this," she said softly as she kissed him.

The battle was won.

11

Astafieva

A BOY IN a brown velvet coat, brown velvet knickers and thick black stockings, walked with his mother along the King's Road, Chelsea.

"This must be it." Mrs. Kay stopped outside a gracious old house set back a little from the road, behind a white stone archway. "Miss Cone said it was over the Pheasantry."

"Oh, I see!" Pat pointed to the row of tall windows with curved, iron balconies on the first floor. He wondered what lay in store for him up there, and his heart beat fast as they climbed the stairs.

At the top they became aware of a confused murmur of voices.

"But darling, I tell you I put them down in that room . . ." reached them loud and clear in broken English. "I cannot go without them . . ." The door swung open abruptly. A surprising apparition in trailing scarves, long strings of pearls, and loose clothes untidily bunched up around her, stood before them.

"Madame Astafieva?" Mrs. Kay inquired.

"Yes. That is me. You want to see me?" She looked around like a cornered bird seeking escape.

"Yes," said Mrs. Kay. Could this really be the same immaculate, white figure they had seen on the stage of the Coliseum? "My son Pat is very anxious to come to your classes."

"My classes?" Astafieva's mind was still darting about among her lost gloves. "This is your son?" She looked him up and down, short pants, black stockings, and all.

"He wants to be my pupil?"

"Yes, please," said Pat.

"Have you found them, darling?" she called to an invisible maid. To Astafieva, everybody was "darling."

"Not yet, Madame," a harassed sounding voice replied.

"Come in here," she told Pat. "Let me look at you. I have not much time now. You have danced before? Yes? What can you do? How long have you been dancing?" Rattling off questions, she led the way into the long, light studio. "What makes you think you can dance? Don't you know that to be a dancer it takes much work, long training for many years . . ." She kept on walking around him, and Pat wondered if she expected him to provide any answers.

"We saw you dancing at the Coliseum three weeks ago," Mrs. Kay managed to put in. "Ever since then, Pat has given me no peace till I brought him to you."

"I have learned dancing at Miss Cone's school for three years," added Pat. "I'm thirteen."

"Ah!" Astafieva hitched a drooping scarf over her shoulder. By contrast with her trailing clothes, her movements had grace and precision.

"Shall I dance for you now?" he suggested.

"Dance?" She suddenly remembered. "No. I have no time. I am late. I have to go and be photographed." She precipitated herself suddenly out of the studio.

"What about Pat?" Mrs. Kay pursued the darting bird into the passage. "May he join your class?"

Astafieva collected her scattered thoughts.

"I will see him dance tomorrow." She twirled around. "Let him come to my class in the morning. 11 o'clock." Her hands fluttered in a helpless gesture. "What is the time now? Three o'clock? I shall be late! Yes, Madame, tomorrow I shall see what he can do . . . " And she was gone, scarves and perfume trailing in her wake.

Pat slept badly that night. Dancing feet chased through his dreams; a mocking, smiling face half-hidden in swathing scarves lured him on. He reached out his arms and went leaping after it. He knew he must catch it, that he could never rest until he held that elusive dancing shadow.

He woke sweating, the dream still vivid in his mind. It was not the first time he had chased this shadow in his sleep. Even waking he felt always that he was reaching out for something that was still just beyond his grasp. What was this unknown power that lured him on? Was it the veiled vision of his own future? Or the haunting spirit of his own ambition? He could give it no name, and it gave him no peace.

There were voices and laughter in the big studio next morning as the class assembled. The girls were in plain tunics, some with their hair tied back in the severe, classical style with bandeaux, others with short, bobbed heads. They stared curiously at the boy who had appeared among them. Boys were in the minority.

There was silence as Madame Astafieva arrived to start

the class. If anything, she looked even more haphazardly dressed than the day before. Her beautiful head was swathed in a silk bandeau, the lovely lines of her body hidden in a shapeless tunic and short black skirt. The whole outfit seemed to be held together with knotted scarves and safety-pins. White stockings covered her legs, and on her feet she had tiny, pink ballet slippers. In her hand, she carried the traditional symbol of the Ballet Mistress—a long jeweled stick.

"At the bar everyone." She rapped the floor sharply.

Pat took his place in the long line of pupils.

The class began.

Madame worked them hard. She demanded intense concentration. Nothing escaped her sharp eye. As she passed along the line of pupils, her long stick would flash out to hit any legs that were not working properly.

Demi-pliés, pliés, battements, ronds de jambe, they went through all the routine of work at the bar. In the far corner by the piano, Mrs. Kay sat and watched. She soon realized that here was a teacher of rare quality. Astafieva not only taught, she inspired. She was putting into her pupils her own fiery spirit. She poured out her energy to give these boys and girls her own unquenchable love of the dance.

Adagio and Allegro in the center. The pupils were called out in twos and threes. It was Pat's turn.

Mrs. Kay, watching Astafieva, would have given much to know what she was thinking as she saw him dance before her. She made no comment.

When the class was over, Pat joined his mother. Together they came over to Astafieva.

"What do you think of him?" Mrs. Kay asked. "Will he make a dancer?"

Astafieva's dark eyes were thoughtful as she looked at the eager, upturned face of the boy standing before her. Was she seeing into the future? Seeing a small figure dancing through the years ahead, and growing all the time in stature, greater, and ever greater?

"I don't know," she said slowly. "We shall see later. He will have to work very hard."

With that Mrs. Kay had to be content, but Pat was completely happy for he had gotten his desire. He became a regular pupil at the studio, and his legs became regular targets for that flashing, jeweled stick. He adored his temperamental teacher who called him Patté and sent him home covered with bruises. Through her own radiating energy she was giving him his first living contact with the inspiring tradition of the great Russian Ballet Schools. This was the teacher he wanted. For her he was prepared to work till he dropped.

At home now there was peace. Dancing was accepted as an inevitable part of Pat's life. His education was taken over by a tutor. In September Anthony went back to school.

From the war, Philip, who was now an officer, wrote scrappy letters mostly talking about his next leave, and wondering gloomily when the interminable fighting was going to end. Three years they had had of it now. Mr. Kay, watching his income slowly drowning in a sea of rising prices, wondered too, how much longer it would go on. No question now, of giving his boys the leisured, sporting life he had known of the England country gentleman who had no specific occupation and lived on his income. His great worry nowadays was whether he would be able to hold out financially until they were old enough to earn their own living.

For Mrs. Kay the days became one big problem to keep the home going, to make the housekeeping money last, to keep the maids, and to provide meals for her family.

In November a letter arrived for Pat one breakfast time.

"It's from Mr. Wolheim," He waved it about excitedly. "They're going to do Bluebell again this Christmas, and he wants me to go along for the audition. It's at the Palace Theatre."

"How lovely, darling," said Mrs. Kay. "When is it?"

"November 25th—that's tomorrow, ten o'clock."

"Tomorrow," she repeated thoughtfully. "I don't think I can come with you. I have to get the ration coupons, and that means standing on line most of the morning."

"I shall be all right alone," said Pat airily. "I wonder if all the others will be there too."

They were, or at least most of them. There was an excited and noisy reunion of last year's Bluebell gang.

"What time is this audition going to start?" they began asking when the gossip flagged. "We've been here an hour already."

"Let's find out what is happening." Someone went to investigate and came back saying, "We've just got to wait here."

The gossip and reminiscences started up again. As Pat talked and joked with the others, he became aware of a man making his way over to him.

"May I talk to you a minute?" The man beckoned him aside. Pat followed him suspiciously a little apart from the others.

"I wondered if you would be interested in a job. I think I could offer you a good part." The man looked him up and down. "Yes, you're just about the right size."

Pat frowned at him, finding all this most odd.

"Thank you very much but I don't want a job," he said. "I believe I shall be playing in Bluebell. I played in it last year, and they wrote and asked me to come here today."

"Yes, I see," said the man slowly. He paused a moment, as though he were going to say something more but changed his mind. "Well." He raised his hat. "In that case, I'm sorry."

Funny man, thought Pat as he joined the others, and then he wished he'd asked what the job was.

They stood around for another hour before Mr. Wolheim appeared.

"I'm very sorry, boys and girls, but there won't be an audition today, after all," he told them. "Will you come back again next week? Yes, a week from today, here, at the same time."

What an anti-climax. All the excitement and waiting, just to be told that. Disappointed, the groups began to break up.

"You'd think they might have made up their minds before bringing us all here." Pat grumbled as they went down to the stage door.

"Excuse me," said a voice at his side, and there was the mysterious man again. "I would like to give you my card." He pushed it into Pat's hand. "Just in case you change your mind about my suggestion. Think it over."

"Who is that?" another boy asked as they came out into the street.

Pat looked at the name on the card.

"Kreimer," he read out. "Theatrical Agent and Impresario."

"Never heard of him," said the boy.

"Nor have I." Pat put the card in his pocket. "Why do

you think they've sent us away for a week?" They walked along together.

"I heard a rumor that it's not at all certain whether they will put Bluebell on this year after all."

"Oh!" Pat stopped short. That was different. His fingers felt the square card in his pocket. That explained a lot of things. If there was no Bluebell . . .

He turned and ran back through the stage door.

"Yes, young man," said Mr. Wolheim as Pat came hurrying across the stage to him. "What is it?"

"Is it true that Bluebell may not be put on this year after all?"

Mr. Wolheim raised his eyebrows, wondering at the speed at which rumors travel.

"Who told you that?"

"One of the boys."

"I'm afraid I can't answer your question. We shall know more about it next week."

"I've been offered another job." Pat trotted out his half-truth with a convincing air. "What shall I do about it?"

"Take it and be thankful," said Mr. Wolheim who was a busy man.

"I think you did quite right," said Mrs. Kay when Pat told her about it. "I should go and see Mr. Kreimer as soon as possible and find out what he has to offer you."

There was a smile on Mr. Kreimer's face as Pat was shown into his office the next morning.

"So you have thought it over."

"I just came in to ask you what the job was," said Pat.

"It is *Peter Pan,*" Mr. Kreimer told him. "They are looking for a boy to play the part of John. How old are you?"

"Thirteen and a half," Pat told him.

Mr. Kreimer asked him some more questions about himself, and scribbled something on a pad.

"Can you be at the New Theatre at 5:30 today?"

"Yes, I think so." Pat rapidly decided that tutors and dancing classes should be slung overboard for the occasion.

"Good. You will go for an audition there with the producer, Mr. Boucicault. He will want to hear you recite. Have you something ready?"

"I will have," said Pat.

Events were crowding in thick and fast. He rushed home to tell his mother the exciting news, and spent the afternoon feverishly rehearsing his poems, and watching the clock, with that screwed-up feeling of adventure, until quite suddenly he was caught up in it and found himself standing on the stage of the New Theatre facing a dim group of people in the orchestra, who seemed altogether hostile. They interrupted his poem, one man flung questions at him, another pushed a script of *Peter Pan* in his hand and told him to read parts of it. Could he sing? they wanted to know. Could he dance? Pat felt that he was being dragged through a large machine that was slowly tearing him into little pieces.

Miserable and frightened he obeyed the summons to come down into the orchestra. He wondered why they didn't throw him out at once.

"I think he'll do," he heard one man say to another. "Inexperienced, but possible."

One of the dim faces loomed closer to him.

"We can offer you the part of John."

Pat opened his mouth in such surprise that no words came out.

"At a salary of £4 10s.* a week," the voice added.

Pat shut his mouth and swallowed. His brain unfroze and began to calculate. £4 10s. was more than twice his salary in Bluebell. But what about Bluebell? In spite of what Mr. Wolheim had said, could he just walk out on Bluebell?

"Thank you very much, sir," he managed to say at last. "May I talk it over with my mother first?"

"Yes, but we must have your answer tomorrow. Before twelve o'clock."

Thirteen-year old Pat was feeling extremely grown up as he left the theatre. The terror of the ordeal he had been through gave way to the rising elation of success. He'd been offered a contract.

There were two parts to choose from now: John in *Peter Pan*; or the Black Cat in Bluebell. *Peter Pan* or Bluebell. John or the Black Cat.

The two chased each other around in his head all the way home. He felt he was faced with the most important decision in his life.

"What do you think, Mother?" he asked her gravely.

"I think it's wonderful, darling."

"Yes, but which shall I take?"

They discussed it all evening.

"I think the best thing is if I phone Mr. Wolheim for you first thing in the morning," suggested Mrs. Kay. "Then we can find out just what is happening about Bluebell."

"I will call him." Pat, still feeling grown up, insisted on conducting his own business.

"Is that Mr. Wolheim?" He perched on a chair in front of the wall telephone, next morning.

---

*About $15.

"Yes, Mr. Wolheim speaking," came the muffled voice over the wire.

"This is Pat Kay. Can you tell me if you really are putting on Bluebell this year?"

"No, I can't," The muffled voice sounded annoyed. "As I told you when you asked before, there's nothing definite."

"Would you have me as the Black Cat again if it was put on?" Pat insisted.

"I expect so."

"Well, how much would you pay then?"

A muffled snort came over the wire.

"Four pounds," said Mr. Wolheim. Pat made a face over his shoulder at his mother, holding up four fingers.

"Five." He bargained.

"You little devil," the voice rattled back. "Come and see me tomorrow then, and we'll fix it up."

Mr. Wolheim rang off. Pat thoughtfully hung up his own earpiece.

"It's not certain about Bluebell and it's not certain they'll pay me more than four pounds." He looked at his mother.

"What a real business man you're becoming." She tried not to show how amused she was at his important, serious air. "Conducting your own affairs over the telephone."

"I think I'll take the *Peter Pan* offer." Pat made the great decision.

"I think you're very wise," she told him, and before twelve o'clock they were both in Mr. Boucicault's office. The contract was signed.

12

Flight

"PETER PAN. First rehearsal. Thursday, ten o'clock." The call was sent out. The company assembled on the stage of the New Theatre. For many of the actors *Peter Pan* was an annual reunion.

"Hello, old man, how are you?" Veteran Pirates and Indians greeted each other. It was all a big family party.

Pat, standing alone, felt homesick for his friends in Bluebell.

"Is this your first time in Peter?"

He looked around and saw a flaxen-haired girl, smaller than himself, standing beside him.

"Yes."

"It's mine too. I'm Michael Darling."

"Oh! Are you? I'm your brother John." They introduced themselves. "Do you know the play well?" Pat asked.

"My mother brought me to see it last year, but I don't remember much about it except the flying."

"I wonder how they do it." Pat gazed up at the flies over his head as if hoping for an immediate solution to the mystery.

A young man joined them, introducing himself as the Crocodile.

"Were you in it last year?" they asked him.

"Yes. Unity Moore was Peter."

"Who's Peter Pan this year?" Pat wanted to know.

"Fay Compton. Look! She's standing over there, talking to Mr. Boucicault." They turned to see the already famous young actress with glorious auburn hair that framed a most attractive, heart-shaped face.

"It's awfully hard being Peter," said the Crocodile, "because Pauline Chase was so wonderful in the part that critics have decided no one can ever be quite as good again. You see she played it eight years running."

"Goodness! It's an awfully old play, isn't it?"

"It's been played every year since 1904."

"That's almost thirteen years!" Michael was very impressed.

"Who's the other one?" Pat asked. "The one next to Fay Compton?"

"She's Stella Patrick Campbell." The Crocodile knew all the answers. "She is the daughter of the famous Mrs. Patrick Campbell."

"What is she playing?"

"Mrs. Darling."

"Oh!" said Michael and John together. "She's going to be our mother." What a young and charming looking mother too.

"And do you see that man talking to Fay Compton now?" the Crocodile whispered urgently.

They looked, and saw a frail looking little man who had just joined the group. He was chiefly remarkable for a drooping, untidy mustache, and a high, domed forehead with deep-set, sunken eyes that gave him a melancholy, brooding air. He looked rather out of place, they thought, between the two beautiful actresses.

"Is he in it too?" asked Michael.

"That," said the Crocodile, in an awed whisper, "is the author of the play, Sir James Barrie."

"Oh!" Pat and Michael looked again at the small, unassuming figure of the great man. He was smiling now at something Fay Compton was saying. What a change had come over him with that smile. His whole face seemed to light up. He looked quite boyish.

"I never thought he looked like that," said Michael. And Pat, who had never thought of him at all, said nothing.

"What do those girls do?" Michael was looking at a group of girls talking and laughing together on the side of the stage. "I don't remember seeing a lot of girls in it last year."

"They're the lost boys." The Crocodile laughed at the sight of their surprised faces. He broke off to wave, as one of the "Lost Boys" had caught sight of him looking in their direction.

"Were they all in it last year?" asked Pat.

"No, but most of them are Conti children so I know them."

"What's that?"

"Haven't you ever heard of the Italia Conti Stage School?" He was surprised. "Miss Conti trains children for the stage. We nearly all come from her."

"What sort of things do you learn there?" Pat was interested, but there was no time for an answer.

"Stand by, everybody," the stage manager called out.

They saw the short, energetic figure of the producer come into the center of the stage.

Mr. Boucicault took over the company and work began.

At the beginning, Pat, already tempered in the fire of a

Seymour Hicks production, felt that he had been through the worst and was ready to face anything in the way of rehearsal temperament. Mr. Boucicault, however, lost no time in changing his mind for him.

As rehearsals followed, day after day, the atmosphere became steadily stormier. Where Mr. Hicks barked his displeasure, Mr. Boucicault roared, and the New Theatre and everyone in it trembled with the sound. Where did such a little man pack such a volume of rage, most of which, it seemed, was directed on the unfortunate Pat?

"Don't worry, my boy." One of the Pirates consoled him after a long and trying ship scene. "He always picks on Johns. Never did like 'em."

"That's all this morning, thank you." The stage manager dismissed them. "This afternoon 2:30. Return Nursery Scene. Will Wendy, John, and Michael stay behind now for flying practice."

Pat wondered unhappily what new horrors were in store.

"Cheer up." His sister Wendy came over to him smiling. "Flying is lovely. Mr. Kirby takes us and he's ever so nice."

"Not Mr. Boucicault?" Things seemed a little brighter.

"No." She laughed. "He won't be there."

"Who's Mr. Kirby?"

"He's the person who invented flying especially for *Peter Pan.*"

The stage hands were putting up the Nursery Scene. In the wings, the Kirby men were disentangling ropes and wires and calling up to invisible comrades in the flies over their heads. The three children stood around waiting, until a quiet-voiced man came up to them.

"Will you come over here to get your harness?" Mr. Kirby led them to the back of the stage. Here stood the big, wooden crates with "Kirby Flying Apparatus" stamped in bold, black letters across their sides.

They were intitiated into the mystery of their harness, a curious collection of straps that buckled around and over their bodies tying them up like a package.

"None of this is seen of course under your pajamas." Mr. Kirby finished tightening the straps. "There is a special slit in the jacket for the wire."

"I think this is rather frightening," whispered little Michael as she and Pat were led into the middle of the Nursery, and the wires were clipped on to the saddle-shaped pads on their backs.

"Does it ever break?" Pat walked about cautiously, looking up at the long shining thread to which he was attached that disappeared into an unknown darkness above.

"It'll lift half a ton, so you don't need to worry." Mr. Kirby smiled as he led Pat over to a place by the bed. "Now stand here. We'll give you a straight lift first. Hold on to my hands. Don't try to jump. Let the wire do all the work. All right, Tom," he called, "take him up."

Pat, clutching Mr. Kirby's hands, felt himself slowly lifted off the ground. His feet were now level with the middle of Mr. Kirby's vest. He felt like a sack of potatoes dangling there. Looking across he saw Michael dangling a few yards away. They smiled at each other.

"Good." Mr. Kirby had him lowered again. "Now try by yourself."

Up and down they both went, growing more confident with each lift. The flying men heaved on the ropes, and the two of them were hoisted up higher and faster.

"It's fun." Michael squealed and wriggled about on the end of the wire.

"I like flying." Pat flapped his arms wildly.

Wendy arrived, her harness modestly hidden under a long nightdress. A third wire came down and she joined the dangling figures in the air.

"Now for some real flights," said Mr. Kirby. "I want you to remember, children, that while your wires are on, you must only move where I tell you; otherwise you will get them crossed." He walked about drawing chalk marks on the floor. "John, come over here." He led Pat into a corner and stood him on a large J. "This time, instead of going straight up and down, you will fly across the Nursery."

"How do I make myself go there?" asked Pat.

"You don't," Mr. Kirby told him. "We see to that for you." They did. Pat was lifted into the air. High over the bed he swung in a graceful curve to land gently by Nana's kennel. He looked back and there were Michael and Wendy floating across the width of the room.

"That was lovely," Pat called out. "Can I do it again?"

"Wait till Michael and Wendy are back in their places."

Small figures went swinging through the air under Mr. Kirby's careful eye. All over the Nursery they flew, and all too soon the practice was over and they were clamoring for the next one.

"I can't tell you yet." Mr. Kirby, who had been giving *Peter Pan* children the thrill of their first flights for thirteen years, smiled sympathetically as he took the wires off. "It depends on Mr. Boucicault. Tomorrow I'm rehearsing Peter by herself, and then you will all do it together."

For Pat, flying remained the nicest part of rehearsals. Even Mr. Boucicault's shouting couldn't spoil the thrill of soaring through the air. Besides, one felt so superior, sailing about over Mr. Boucicault's head.

The rest of the rehearsals, however, had become a daily misery. Pat came to dread each new day.

"You must just stick it out, darling." His mother tried to give him courage. "It'll be better when the play is on and everyone has settled down."

"I don't think it ever will go on," said Pat gloomily. "Not with me in it. When he shouts at me I just forget everything and that makes him more angry and he shouts louder. If I don't understand what he wants right away, he just catches hold of me and drags me around the stage."

"It's not much longer now till the opening night." She wished she could give him comfort. "Think how proud you will be playing a big part in Barrie's famous play. It'll all seem worth while then."

So, Pat, grateful to her, but unconvinced, counted the days until the opening on Christmas Eve.

13

Peter Pan

CHRISTMAS EVE 1917: a theatre full of excited children with their parents, and the curtain going up on the firelit Nursery. There was the big, cuddly Nana busy on bed-time preparations.

Outside the Nursery door waited a nervous Michael in little white blouse and shorts, a nervous John in a black Eton suit, and an equally nervous Wendy, all of them uncomfortably aware of the flying harness buckled tightly under their clothes.

Nana came to the door to fetch Michael.

"Good luck," they whispered as he climbed astride the white, wooly back, and Michael was carried into the lights shouting:

"No, Nana, no! I tell you I won't go to bed."

John and Wendy watched him through the fake picture on the wall. As they waited for their cue, Pat thought suddenly of that other first night in Bluebell, and Mr. Hicks hissing at him from the wings.

"If I make a mistake out there and Mr. Boucicault shouts at me, I shall dry up," he whispered panic-stricken, "I know I will."

"John, dear! What an idea! Of course he won't shout at you." Wendy squeezed his hand. "You won't make any mistakes. Come on, it's us."

John and Wendy moved into the lighted Nursery.

Down in front, Mr. and Mrs. Kay and Anthony had the thrill of seeing their Pat take the stage in his first straight acting part.

"No, Nana. No, I won't be bathed, I tell you I won't be bathed." To roars of delight from the sympathetic young in the audience, he was chased around the armchair by a growling Nana, and pursued into the bathroom in his turn, to do a quick change into pajamas and slippers.

Nerves had gone now; only excitement remained. The hardest part he found was having to go to bed on the stage and lie very still for hours and hours, or so it seemed. Only later in the run of the play would he and Michael think of taking bags of suckers to bed with them to pass the time. On this first night however he was on his best behavior. John lay quite motionless while mother tucked them up one after the other. His bed was by itself near the fire. He lay under the covers with his back to the audience, hoping that his make-up wasn't getting smudged on the pillow. The Nursery was dimly lit now by the night lights over each bed.

In the wings a man waited with a mirror in his hands to send the mischievous Tinker Bell dancing into the room while his mate stood behind the curtained window with a rope of bells, and Fay Compton crouched on a mattress ready for her take-off.

The audience was very still now, watching that hushed Nursery. From where Pat lay he could just see the window. He saw the curtains shake violently and heard the jangle of bells as Tinker Bell flashed into the room. One after the other the night lights flickered and went out. Only the glow of the fire remained, spreading a mysterious red light in the room.

Soft music wove a mysterious spell, mounting in excitement till the air tingled with it. On a swift climax the windows burst open, and out of the night sky, high over the roof tops, Peter Pan flew into the Nursery, a brown, elf-like figure in the glow of the fire. Another flight to the bathroom door, then high across the room to land on the mantelpiece. Back again to the corner. Cue for the sleeping children to toss and turn, and send Peter flying to hiding behind the curtains to have the wire taken off.

After this, a long, dull wait for John lying without moving while Wendy woke and she and Peter went through their business of sewing on the shadow, exchanging thimbles, and releasing Tinker Bell, who had got shut in a drawer.

There was a big laugh when Peter pushed John out of

bed and he rolled on the floor. Not so funny for John who landed awkwardly with his head on the fender and his legs twisted and had to stay like that, bundled up in bedclothes "sleeping" until he was officially awakened by Wendy.

"I shall get cramps and I shan't be able to move," he thought. Cautiously he straightened a leg, hoping that no one would notice.

It seemed hours before Wendy came and shook him.

"Wake up, John. Get up. There's a boy here who is to teach us to fly."

Another laugh for John as he sat up, rubbed his eyes, found himself on the floor and remarked:

"Oh! I see I am up already."

After that, quick action. The alarm of Nana barking and the children scattering to hide so that Kirby men could quickly clip on their flying wires. Tremendous laughs from the children in the audience as Wendy, John, and Michael tried to fly off their beds and landed flat on their backs on the floor. The thrilling moment when Peter put the secret of flying on them, and the roars of delight as they went up, John's arms and legs threshing wildly about, Michael doing a vigorous breast stroke through the air, and Wendy hovering gracefully over her bed, while out of sight in the wings three men heaved on the ends of their ropes.

Swiftly followed the decision to emigrate to the Never Never Land where Wendy could exercise her maternal instincts on Peter's collection of Lost Boys. John and Michael, lured by the promise of Pirates and Indians, ran to stand on their chalk marks ready for the take-off. Tinker Bell swung the windows wide, and away they went, the brown figure of Peter, the white Wendy, John in pajamas and top hat, and lastly little Michael.

"Keep well down," someone whispered at them as they landed on the mattress below the window sill. They crouched waiting while Mrs. Darling rushed into the Nursery too late to bring her children back and the curtain came down on the first act to the ringing sound of applause.

"Well done; nice flights." The Kirby men came hurrying around to release them from their wires.

"I do think Pat is good." Mrs. Kay was clapping as loudly as she could. "He looks so natural."

"Got a good voice for it," said his father. "I must say that flying business is very effective."

"I think flying is the best part." Anthony fidgeted about excitedly. "I do want to know how it's done. I wish Pat would tell me."

All around them children were wanting to know the same thing. Many of them, probably, were secretly resolved to try on their own, just as soon as they got home to their own nurseries; for the unsophisticated young of 1917 firmly believed in magic and the world of fairies where everything was possible.

"It's hard to believe that it really is Pat." Anthony swung his legs, kicking the seat in front. He felt so proud of his brother that he wanted to tell everybody.

"Don't talk so loudly dear." His mother stopped the kicking.

"What comes next?" Anthony rummaged for the program under a big box of chocolates already half empty. "Will they fly again?"

He was soon to find out, for the curtain rose and they were carried away into Peter Pan's Never Never Land; to the Frozen River; to the Mermaid's Lagoon; to the exciting

Home under the Trees where the Lost Boys lived, guarded by the friendly Indians.

Breathlessly they followed the terrible adventures with Pirates: battle, treachery, and the Capture of the Lost Boys.

Even Anthony was pale with excitement as the curtain rose on a real, sinister Pirate Ship, and the evil Captain Hook walked the deck in his own green light, flashing his curved steel finger as he gloated over his chained Captives.

John's big moment came in this scene when Captain Hook said he had room for a Cabin Boy. It was tempting.

"I'd rather like to be a Pirate." John confessed every small boy's dream. "I thought of calling myself Redhanded Jack," a confession that brought a roar of derision from the real Pirates, and the dream was rudely shattered when John discovered that being a Pirate meant swearing "Down with the King."

"Well I won't." John, a courageous and loyal subject, shook his chained fists at Captain Hook's face and defiantly started a rousing chorus of *Rule Britannia,* a brave and hopeless gesture for it was swiftly drowned by the yells of the infuriated Pirates, and the enraged Captain Hook condemned all of them to the terrible death of walking the plank.

This was altogether too much for some of the audience who were removed, screaming with fright. The brave who remained, however, saw Peter's dramatic arrival and the rescue, ending in a glorious battle as the boys swarmed down from the rigging, sword in hand, to surprise and attack the Pirates.

"This is one of the best parts of the play," thought Pat as he chased a large Pirate across the deck at the point of his wooden sword and sent him screaming overboard.

The battle was over. The villains were defeated and the audience relaxed to the Return Nursery Scene where Mr. Darling was now to be found living in Nana's kennel, while Mrs. Darling played the piano and mourned for her lost children.

A last flight for Wendy and John who carried Michael on his back. They came sailing in through the window for a glorious reunion. The Lost Boys moved into the Darlings' home. There was a last glimpse of Peter and Wendy in the House in the Tree Tops among the fairies and birds, and it was all over.

Curtain calls and applause.

"Well done, Pat." Mrs. Kay's voice was lost in the storm of clapping, but she felt she had to say it.

Anthony was tremendously proud as he saw Pat line up on the stage with the principals to take his bow. He thought it was really swell to have a brother who was a real actor. He'd be able to boast about it like anything to the other boys at school next term.

"Is Pat famous?" he asked his mother suddenly.

"Not yet dear," she told him. "But he will be."

They had a celebration family supper after the show. A first night was, after all, an important occasion, Mr. Kay decided. He felt really rather proud of his actor son.

"I told you so." Mrs. Kay smiled at Pat as she drank to his success.

"What?"

"I told you it would all seem worth while once the show was on."

She was right. The dark and dreadful days of the rehearsals were well and truly over.

Already by the second day the atmosphere backstage

had become relaxed and friendly. Nobody shouted at John and life began to be worth living again.

"I think I'm going to enjoy *Peter Pan* after all," Pat was saying to himself as he was in his dressing-room changing for the Underground Scene on the second day.

There was a knock on the door. Wendy looked in.

"There's a tea-party in Mrs. Darling's dressing-room. Everyone's invited."

The big room that Stella Patrick Campbell shared with Doris McIntyre, the first twin, was already crowded. Pirates, Indians, and Lost Boys were perched on chairs and hampers. Wolves and the Crocodile sprawled on the floor.

"Come along!" Mrs. Darling welcomed her "children" into the family. "I'm so glad you're here."

"Help yourselves," Doris waved a hand in the direction of a table covered with plates of cakes and candies. "I'll just get you some tea."

They found a space on the floor with the Wolves. There was a knock at the door and a sudden silence. It was Mr. Boucicault.

"So this is where all the Company disappears to after the Lagoon Scene," he said severely, looking around the crowded room.

"They all waited rather guiltily for a storm to break.

It didn't. Mr. Boucicault was suddenly laughing.

"I thought I'd frighten you all," he told them. "Well, Stella, I think this is a splendid idea of yours. Very nice of you to invite me."

A chair of honor was found and he joined the party. As he stayed talking and joking with them, the atmosphere rapidly warmed up again, and all too soon the Call Boy was hammering on the door.

"Underground beginners please."

"Who'd have thought it?" Pat remarked as he and Michael went down to the stage. "The old dragon is quite human. He was actually nice to me."

"I hope it lasts," rejoined Michael.

It did. Now that Peter Pan was well launched, Mr. Boucicault was a changed man. It was as though all the pent-up fire in him had burned itself out. He was calm and friendly. An atmosphere of peace pervaded the backstage world.

The tea-party was the first of many. In fact Mrs. Darling's dressing-room became a happy gathering place for most of the Company. *Peter Pan* was a thoroughly happy family. All too soon, it seemed to Pat, the six weeks' run had come to an end and he was hanging up John's Eton suit and flying harness for the last time.

"What happens next?" was the question that hung heavily in the air.

"Isn't it awful that there's no theatre to go to today?" He trailed disconsolately around the house next morning.

"I wish they'd let *Peter Pan* run longer. Bluebell will be going on for another month at least. They don't finish till March."

"Do you wish you'd done Bluebell this year after all?" his mother asked.

"No." Pat was quite decided. "I love *Peter Pan,* and I love being John. It's a much better part. Why does Peter always have to be a girl?" He was pursuing an idea of his own.

"I suppose it would be too difficult to find a boy each year who was good enough."

"Fay Compton was wonderful. I love her voice. It's just

my idea of the way Peter would talk, but I still think it should be a real boy. I wish I could play Peter." He began doing the shadow dance. "Do you know, Mother, I am out of practice." He stopped again.

"It's hardly surprising since you've had to miss so many classes."

"That's the only reason I'm pleased the show is over. I am free to go to Astafieva's again. Oh Mother, I do want to be a dancer!"

14

"What Happens Next?"

THE QUESTION "What happens next?" loomed very largely in Mrs. Kay's mind during the days that followed. She had hoped that *Peter Pan* would lead to another engagement, but nothing so far had materialized. She wanted to encourage Pat with his acting. Dancing was all very well, she thought, but she couldn't see much future in it for him.

The world of 1918 seemed to present very little opportunity for a ballet dancer, especially a man. After all, Pat had a talent for acting. She felt he needed a proper training for the stage, but where? and how? What was the best thing to do for him? What did happen next? Mrs. Kay, puzzling over the problem, realized that the time had come to get professional advice and help for Pat's future. She talked it over with her husband.

"Whom do we know in the theatre? I feel we should go to someone who could tell us what is the best thing to do to have him trained."

"You're right, Maude. Want an opinion from a really first-class man in the profession. Someone like Beerbohm-Tree."

"Yes, except that he's dead," said Mrs. Kay. "He died last year. All the big actor-managers seem to be disappearing," she realized with a shock. "Kendal died last year. Forbes-Robertson has been retired two or three years. There's Sir Charles Wyndham, but he's a very old man now. I should think he must have retired too. Henry Ainley is away in the war. There doesn't seem to be anyone taking their places."

"Who's that man at the St. James's Theatre?" said Mr. Kay suddenly. "Your cousin was talking about him the other night at dinner."

"Oh! I remember. She was talking about Sir George Alexander."

"Alexander, that's the man. He must be getting on in years. Why I remember seeing him at the St. James's when I was a young man. Very fine actor."

"He's very active still," said Mrs. Kay. "I remember Mary was telling us what wonderful work he is doing for the war, organizing charity matinees to raise money for the Red Cross. She's on a lot of those committees herself. I think she knows him quite well. I wonder if she would help us?"

She did. She gave them an introduction that opened for them the well-guarded doors of the St. James's Theatre.

Through the stage door they passed into one of the last strongholds of the great Actor-Manager tradition.

For nearly twenty-eight years Sir George Alexander had reigned over this theatre.

Mrs. Kay and Pat were ushered into the presence of the great man in his dressing-room. More like a living room Pat thought, sitting up rather straight and on his best behavior, on the edge of a chair, while his mother and the great man exchanged polite preliminaries.

As Pat looked around he could not help comparing this with his own bare dressing-room at the New Theatre. What a contrast! Here were heavy brocade curtains, a soft carpet, and armchairs. A silk screen went across one corner, hiding the make-up table. A bright coal fire in the grate sent flickering, golden lights over the dark, polished furniture. Everywhere, he saw books, photographs, pictures, old programs, souvenirs: treasures gathered during the quarter of a century that this dressing-room had been Sir George Alexander's home.

Pat gazed with awe at the famous and distinguished looking man who had reigned over the St. James's Theatre for so long. How little could he guess that the reign was so soon to come to an end, that this courteous and handsome actor was fighting a silent, losing battle against incurable diabetes. Before the year was out, this dressing-room would stand forlornly empty, and Sir George would never see the brilliant destiny of the boy who now sat before him.

These things still lay mercifully hidden behind the veil of the future, as Sir George spoke to Pat asking him questions about himself and his work in *Peter Pan* and Bluebell. He was a charming and kindly person.

Pat, obeying his mother's instructions, did not mention dancing. They spoke of various ways of starting a stage career.

"In my young days, of course, a boy joined a Company and started with walking-on parts," Sir George told him. "It was up to him to pick up what knowledge he could and make good. That was learning the hard way." A smile lit the tired lines around his eyes. "Nowadays, it is much easier for you youngsters. There are schools which train young people." He looked at Mrs. Kay. "The best advice I can give you is to send your boy to Italia Conti. You couldn't do better than to let him go to her school."

Words that suddenly fitted in with all that Pat had already heard about this school in *Peter Pan.* He knew that this was the right answer for him.

"I'd like to go," he told his mother afterwards. "I've heard a lot about her."

"I've always heard that it is an excellent school. We'll have to find out what the fees are. I hope we shall be able to afford it." Mrs. Kay was thinking rather anxiously of the tutor's bill and Astafieva's fees. "One thing," she went on, thinking aloud rather than talking to Pat, "since they give an all-round training, I daresay you'll be able to carry on with your ballet there, and give up Astafieva."

Pat looked at her in horror.

"Give up Astafieva?" he repeated. "No! No!" he said violently. "I won't ever give up Astafieva. Never. I won't learn dancing anywhere else, and if it means giving her up then I'd rather not go to the Conti School. Promise me you'll never make me give up Astafieva."

"All right, darling, of course I won't. Not if you feel like that about it." Realizing what a mistake she had made, she tried to quiet this passionate outburst and reassure him.

"I don't mind learning to act," Pat went on, "but I don't ever want to stop dancing."

"Nor shall you."

With this assurance, Pat relaxed, while his mother wondered again at this relentless urge to dance that drove him so insistently.

"When can we go and see Italia Conti?" he asked.

"I'll write her today," Mrs. Kay promised.

15

The Conti School

"I'VE ACCEPTED a new pupil for next term." Italia Conti came into the office where her younger sister Evelyn sat at a littered desk trying to keep the confused and swiftly moving affairs of this lively school in some sort of order.

"What rhymes with apple?" The third sister, Bianca, came to life behind a pile of books tumbled over a table in a corner of the crowded room.

"Grapple," suggested Italia, crossing to the mirror to rearrange her hair. "What's it for?"

"The Red Cross show we're doing next month. I want three of my babies in the beginners' Elocution Class to act a poem."

Italia stopped arranging her hair.

"But I told you I want them to do a Romeo and Juliet scene," she said over her shoulder.

"Dapple . . ." Bianca's fingers drummed the meter of her

poem out on the table. "I decided that it is too advanced for them to learn."

"Nonsense, Bianca." Italia's voice went several shades deeper. "Of course they can learn it. A child can learn anything by heart. Besides tiny children look so sweet playing Shakespeare, it's a good advertisement for the school."

"You can train them yourself in that case." Bianca was obstinate. "I'm not going to waste all the time of my class teaching toddlers to recite long passages of Shakespeare that they're much too young to understand."

The atmosphere was getting stormy.

"What's the new pupil's name?" Evelyn now had found a pen and the right book.

"What did you say? Oh yes! The new pupil." Italia left the battle pending. "It's a boy. Kay—Pat Kay. I've got his address somewhere." Her beautiful and helpless hands rummaged in her handbag. "Ah yes!" She produced Mrs. Kay's card. On the back she had written, "Elocution and Acting."

"He'll be coming to several of your classes, Bianca."

"To learn Shakespeare, I suppose," she flashed back.

"Of course he's to learn Shakespeare," Italia screamed at her, "and the earlier they start the better."

"You've got to teach a child things it can understand," Bianca opened up in full volume. "It's actors we want, not parrots."

The walls of the office rang to the shrill sounds of battle, while Evelyn went on placidly entering Pat's name and particulars in the book. The noisy clash of personalities was a frequent and familiar event. Evelyn took no notice.

"How old is this boy?" She made herself heard through the vocal tumult.

"Thirteen and a half," Italia tossed back at her.

"What's he done before?" asked Bianca suddenly.

"Played John in *Peter Pan.*" Italia stopped abruptly. "That reminds me, Bianca. I wonder if one of those boys of ours would do for John or Michael next year?"

"Do you mean one of the Livesey brothers?"

"Yes."

"I thought you were keeping them for *Where the Rainbow Ends?*"

The battle was ended as quickly as it had begun by a sudden switch of mood. They discussed amicably the respective merits of young Roger and Barry Livesey.

Evelyn carefully blotted the new name she had added to the fast-growing list of pupils and put the book away. That was in March.

For several weeks the name of Pat Kay was forgotten in the day-to-day activities of the busy school.

The Conti sisters, brilliant and temperamental, owed the rising success of their school to Bianca's magnificent teaching and to Italia's unerring instinct for recognizing raw talent, developing it, and seeing that it got its chance on the stage.

It was less than seven years since the first band of Conti children had gathered in the rented studios in Great Ormond Street, but already, in 1918, the hallmark "Conti" on a young actor or actress stood for quality in the theatre world.

This was the school then to which Pat Kay came as a new boy in the summer term.

"Evelyn . . . " The ill-used office door crashed open.

"Get me the Kays on the telephone." Italia filled and

dominated the room. "I must speak to Mrs. Kay at once."

"Shut the door!" Evelyn spread her arms over a threatened snowstorm of papers.

"Where's Bianca?" With a regal gesture Italia closed the door.

"She hasn't come up from her class yet," Evelyn lifted her arms from the papers and glanced at the clock. "She ought to be back any time now."

"She must hear him." Italia paced up and down the office. "It was beautiful, most moving."

"What was?"

"'Mother o' Mine.' That boy Pat Kay has just been reciting it in my class. Excellent." Her expressive hands underlined her words. "Such feeling."

"Are you going to tell his mother about it then?" inquired the practical Evelyn.

Italia stopped walking to and fro, and leaned over the top of the desk.

"That boy has talent." A sensitive forefinger probed in Evelyn's direction. "I want him under contract—to us. Get Mrs. Kay on the phone for me—darling."

"I'm trying to do the accounts," Evelyn grumbled.

"It won't take you a minute just to do the phone call for me." Her voice was soft and persuasive.

Evelyn never could resist Italia's charm. She pushed aside the long column she had been trying to add up and searched for the number.

Bianca came in and the office echoed to the name of Pat Kay.

"We can do a lot for that boy, I feel it." Italia's wide gesture sketched a brilliant future.

Evelyn dropped her hand over the mouthpiece of the telephone.

"Mrs. Kay is on the line."

Italia went into action. All the charm of her deep expressive voice went over the wire . . .

"Mrs. Kay is going to think it over." Italia smiled as she hung up the receiver again. "She wants to talk it over with Pat. There is some difficulty apparently because of his dancing. The boy goes to dancing class with Astafieva and doesn't want to give it up." She looked at her sisters, her shrewd, business mind working fast. "I don't think it need make any difference to us."

"No," said Evelyn. "As long as the contract makes it clear that all his stage work is handled by us, he can go on with his dancing lessons."

"There'll be plenty of work for a boy of that type," put in Bianca.

"His mother is coming to see me to discuss it," Italia remembered.

She saw Mrs. Kay the next afternoon and the result was a contract. Pat Kay, with the exception of his dancing classes, became the exclusive property of the Italia Conti School.

Pat himself was delighted, as were his parents. His career seemed to be taking shape. His days became a busy round of School with his Tutor, Dancing with Astafieva, and Stage Classes at Conti's.

His mother, watching him absorbed and happy in all the unfolding promise of his young life, sent up a prayer of thankfulness that the war had not touched him.

The war—that horrible monster—was dragging its hideous length through its fourth year of destruction and death. The daily casualty lists darkened long columns of the newspapers, and Mrs. Kay, like thousands of other mothers, did her best to hide her constant, gnawing fears for her oldest son. She tried to find forgetfulness in busy, crowded days, and was glad that Pat claimed so much of her attention.

He was taking his acting very seriously and needed her help and encouragement to unravel the endless passages of Shakespeare and the long poems he had to study and learn by heart.

Now that Pat's acting career was in Italia Conti's skilled hands, things soon began to happen. He had been in the school scarcely three months when Miss Conti telephoned his mother.

"Would you be prepared to take Pat on tour?" she asked, and Mrs. Kay who had never thought about it, heard the charming and persuasive voice in her ear, "I can offer Pat a very good job . . ."

Pat, who was listening over his mother's shoulder, jumped about with excitement.

". . . They want a boy to play the part of David in the musical comedy *Betty*. I can tell you, Mrs. Kay, it's one of the best parts for a boy that has ever been written in a musical comedy. I think Pat would be just right for it."

Pat nudged his mother making frantic signs to say yes.

". . . They're sending a first-class company out," the voice went on smoothly. "Very good names in it."

"How long is the tour?" Mrs. Kay managed to ask.

"It'll be about twelve weeks, starting at Scarborough. I haven't the list here but I know they plan to do two weeks in Ireland, going to Belfast and Dublin . . ."

Dublin! Mrs. Kay's childhood home. She hadn't been back there for years. Dublin! Her eyes were bright with excitement as she looked at Pat.

"Go on, say yes," he urged her in a whisper.

"When does it start?" she asked.

"They are beginning rehearsing at Daly's Theatre next week and plan to be on tour by the beginning of September . . ."

Italia, at the other end of the phone, smiled as she heard Pat's urgent prompting in the background, and Mrs. Kay's rather startled consent.

"Well, that's fixed." Italia dropped the receiver back on its hook. "Evelyn dear, can you get someone to send a letter off to Mrs. Kay with the details of the rehearsals for *Betty,* and the contract? I want it to go at once before she changes her mind."

Mrs. Kay hung up her receiver more slowly, wondering what she had done. She had just agreed to go off with Pat for twelve weeks. But what about the house? Her husband? Domestic problems crowded in, and then another thought.

"Good heavens!" she said. "After all that, I never asked what salary you'd be getting."

They looked at each other and laughed.

"How like us!"

"Never mind." Pat caught his mother around the waist and waltzed her in a mad circle. "We're going on tour, and we're going to Ireland, and it's all terribly exciting."

16

"*Betty*"

BULKY THEATRICAL hampers were packed; scenery loaded on to trucks and dispatched in advance; musical instruments crated and labeled and on Sunday in September 1918, the touring company of *Betty* started out on its travels, heading north in a grimy, crowded train.

Neither Pat nor his mother knew anything about touring and no one had thought to tell them.

They arrived in Scarborough station, dazed, dirty and tired.

"I thought there would be someone from the theatre to tell us what to do." Mrs. Kay stood like an island in the stream of people flowing towards the gate.

"Hello! Lost your luggage?" A couple of men from the company, loaded with suitcases, packages, and raincoats came staggering by.

"No. We were wondering where to go," Mrs. Kay replied.

"I should go and get settled in your rooms first," one of them told her. "We shan't be wanted at the theatre till tomorrow morning." He broke off when he saw the blank look on Mrs. Kay's face. "Don't you have any rooms reserved?"

"No."

"You'll have a job finding any, especially on a Sunday,"

said the old trooper cheerfully, and the men went on their way.

Mrs. Kay and Pat made their way to a hotel.

"This is all right," said Pat as they were shown into their rooms. "I wonder why the others don't do this."

They discovered the answer soon enough when the bill was presented at the end of the week.

"One thing is quite clear," Mrs. Kay declared. "We can't go on living in hotels. Not on the money you're earning."

They lost no time in getting addresses from people in the company and wrote ahead to reserve rooms in boarding houses in advance as everyone else did.

As they traveled week by week over England, Pat and his mother had their first experience of theatrical boarding houses. They moved through a succession of dingy houses in back streets, sleeping in airless little bedrooms whose brass bedsteads invariably had knobbly mattresses. There was the inevitable marble mantelpiece with dreadful ornaments in colored glass, a chipped washbasin and jug on a marble-topped washstand, and a dim, flickering gaslight. They received indifferent food served on thick, coarse plates.

"Can't help it, dearie, it's the war," the landladies never failed to tell them. "Things are very difficult here."

"I don't mind it," said Pat, and he didn't. It was all new still and a great adventure. Besides there was always the hope that next week's rooms would be better.

He enjoyed his part in *Betty*. There was the rewarding satisfaction of being in the first-class musical comedy that played everywhere to good houses.

"Manchester this week." Mrs. Kay gaily packed their suitcases on a Sunday morning. "Then to Ireland. No uncomfortable rooms in Dublin," she said, laughing. "We shall be home."

"Shall we go and visit your old home?"

"Sure we shall," she told him with a twinkle in her eyes and an Irish lilt to her voice that Pat loved to copy. "And many other homes besides. There's all the cousins who'll be wanting to see you."

"I like being Irish," said Pat. "I always feel I'm more Irish than English."

"I think you are," his mother smiled at him. "You have the dark Irish eyes, and the wayward Irish heart in you."

"And an Irish voice when I've been to Dublin." He laughed.

Meanwhile Manchester waited; a damp, depressing Manchester on a drizzling October evening.

Pat and his mother went through the half-blacked out streets on their way to the theatre.

"Wait a minute." Pat suddenly held her arm. A poster had caught his eye. "Look!" He pointed to a name. "Do you see? 'Boucicault.' Do you think it's the same man who produced *Peter Pan*?"

They went over to read it. The poster advertised a play at another theatre in Manchester. "Dion Boucicault" stood out in bold letters.

"Yes, it must be the same," said Mrs. Kay. "What a curious coincidence. His play is here all this week too."

The coincidence gave Pat an idea.

"I could go and see him," he said thoughtfully. "What do you think? If he's producing *Peter Pan* this year I might get the part of John again. They'll be starting rehearsals next month." He looked at his mother. "Suppose I go to see him tonight?"

"I think it would be better to write first, darling." Mrs. Kay reined back his impatience.

Between them they composed a letter, and a couple of days later Pat was invited to see Mr. Boucicault.

"He was ever so nice to me." He came hurrying back to pass on the good news. "He says that as soon as I'm back in London after the tour, I'm to go and see him at the New Theatre and he'll give me my contract."

"Darling, that's wonderful!" She was as delighted as he was. "It's all fixed then; I am pleased."

She caught sight of the paper Pat was carrying. "Is that the evening paper you've got there?"

"Oh yes! I bought one on the way back, but I was too excited about *Peter Pan* to read it." He handed it over.

The first headline that caught her eye as she opened it was: DISASTER IN THE IRISH CHANNEL.

A ship had been torpedoed and sunk by a German submarine.

When they reached the theatre everyone was talking about it.

"What a terrible thing."

"They won't send us to Ireland now."

"But we're due to sail in three days. We can't let the people down over there, not at such short notice."

"Perhaps the steamship company will cancel the sailing so we can't go."

"I hope they don't. I can't afford to be out of work for two weeks."

The discussions went on all over the dressing-rooms and back stage. Finally, a harassed management decided that the company would sail for Ireland on Sunday as arranged, but that those who preferred not to go would be given leave and could rejoin the tour in two weeks' time, at Leeds.

This decision started up the discussions all over again. In the end, only two or three decided not to go.

"What shall we do, Mother?" Pat asked.

"I don't think we should go." She bravely gave up her longed-for visit to her old home. "It wouldn't be right for you."

"But you were so longing to go to Dublin."

"I know, but it's not worth the risk now. Perhaps I'll get a chance to go another time." She spoke with a cheerfulness she didn't feel. "We'll go back to London instead. Won't father be pleased to have us back. I'll wire him right away to let him know we're coming. It'll be a lovely surprise for him."

Mr. Kay was at the station to meet them. It was easy to pick out his tall, slim figure among the crowd. After the first, delighted rush of reunion Mrs. Kay noticed suddenly that her husband's face looked pale and drawn.

"Are you all right, my dear?" She still had both her hands on his arms. "You're not ill, are you?"

"No. I'm all right," he told her. "Come along, we must get a cab before they're all taken."

She frowned. She didn't like the tone of his voice; it sounded flat and strange.

As the taxi rattled through the familiar London streets, Pat, sitting opposite his mother and father, felt too that something was terribly wrong. He listened with growing fear to his father's painful efforts to make casual conversation.

The house itself seemed empty and unfamiliar.

"Where are the servants?" Mrs. Kay stood in the hall, looking around, sensing the strangeness.

"They're in the kitchen," said Mr. Kay haltingly. "Perhaps Pat wouldn't mind taking some of the luggage up."

Pat reluctantly climbed the stairs. He saw his father and mother go into the study. Unknown fear beat in his heart as he heard the murmur of voices. What dreadful secret was his father telling his mother? Would they tell him too?

He went up to his room and dropped a suitcase on the bed. He hadn't the heart to unpack. He prowled about the upper landing, and came to lean over the banisters. All about him was eerie silence. It seemed hours before he heard the study door open.

"I'll go up to him," he heard his father say, and Pat, hearing his approaching steps, fled into the bedroom.

Here, at last, he was told. Mr. Kay broke the news as gently as he could, but the cruel core of truth could not be softened. His brother Philip was dead. He had died in Egypt.

Pat sat on his bed, stunned. Philip, his beloved older brother, dead. He tried to picture him as he had last seen him, on leave. No. Pat shook his head. Not Philip in khaki; that Philip was a man, who was almost a stranger, for his leaves at home were too short to catch up the threads again. No, the Philip he knew and loved was a boy still, and the best friend and brother in the world. Philip had been part of his life ever since he could remember. Vividly there formed in his mind the swift, bright picture of their home at Felpham. Philip and himself romping in the garden with the dogs, their bird-nesting expeditions, games on the beach, glorious adventures, rock climbing, and swimming, picnics out in the country. The day Philip had helped him ride his first bicycle and they had got into such trouble. There was that wonderful holiday on the farm, the last one and the best of all. He could see Philip again, standing in the sunlight by the orchard fence, laughing. How strong and alive he had been, and now he was dead. Pat would never see him laugh again or hear his voice. Death had laid its cold hand on his warm body. Philip was gone forever. The devastating sense of loss flooded over him. He fell face down on the pillow and the tears came.

Those two weeks in London were heavy with sorrow. Mrs. Kay suffered deeply. Pat and his father found courage themselves in trying to help her. They tried to persuade her to remain at home and give up the tour, but she insisted on returning with Pat to join the company at Leeds.

It was the beginning of November.

A few days later, huge headlines in the papers blazoned the news: "Peace." "Armistice." It was November 11, 1918. Four terrible years of war had ended. All over the country, bells, bonfires, fireworks, shouting, cheering crowds signaled the people's relief and joy.

On the stage of the theatre in Leeds a hastily improvised party started up the moment the curtain had rung down at the end of the show.

Tables were set up on the stage among the scenery. There was laughter and songs; the popping of wine corks, the hiss of beer. Everyone in the place, actors, musicians, stage hands, gathered to drink to the peace of the world. There were speeches and toasts.

Through the clink of glasses, and the splash of wine, Pat looked at his mother. In the hearts of both was the same aching thought. The armistice had come three weeks too late.

17

Acting and Dancing

THERE WAS a knock on the door.

"Come in," barked Mr. Boucicault. He looked up from his paper-smothered desk as the door opened. "Ah, yes! Pat Kay." His shrewd eyes watched the boy cross the room. "You came to see me in Manchester."

"Yes, sir."

"Do you remember your part in *Peter Pan?*"

"Yes, sir."

"Have you grown since last year?"

"No, sir."

"All right," Mr. Boucicault was a busy man. Already the coming production of *Peter Pan* was weighing heavily on him. "Be ready for rehearsal next week."

In this off-hand manner was Pat welcomed back into the *Peter Pan* family for the second year.

It was very different in the studio in the King's Road. Madame Astafieva was in a good mood and delighted to see him again.

"Patté," she called across the studio, "I am pleased to see you in my class again." Her dark eyes were alight with pleasure. "Yes, I know," she waved his words of excuse aside before he had a chance to say them. "You have been on tour; you wrote to me." She put her hands on his shoulders looking him up and down. "You have grown, a little, not too much, that is good. So, you have been in musical comedy." Her voice was deep with scorn. "You, who say you want to be a dancer, you work in musical comedy. Tell me, you have practiced your ballet, yes?"

Pat shook his head.

"Not very often; we didn't get time."

"Patté." She looked at him in despair. "To be a dancer you must work, do exercises, two, three hours every day." Her hands gestured. "But now you come back, you work hard to make up."

"I'll come as often as I can," said Pat nervously, and explained that he was about to start working in *Peter Pan* again. This did not please Madame. She tapped her foot impatiently on the floor, her face darkened.

"You children, you are all alike." A sweeping gesture condemned all her pupils. "The only thing you think of is to get jobs now; to earn money at once. Never mind how: pantomime, musical comedy, chorus work." Her class seemed to wither under her scornful eyes. "Cheap, bad dancing. So you get bad habits, bad style, and then you find out it is no good, there is no future in it, and it is too late for you to start again to learn to be real dancers. No, you must work now, while you are young; there is no time to waste. In Russia a child goes into the Imperial Ballet School at eight years old, and there he stays until he is seventeen or eighteen. Think of it—nine, ten years of training. He lives for nothing but the dance. And when he has finished all this, do you think he is a star, as you call them? No, he is put in the corps de ballet. Yes, after ten years' training the dancer is just good enough to be in the chorus. From there, if he shows he has real talent, he may be given a small part of his own, and then . . . "

Madame was well launched on one of her favorite subjects. She had forgotten about Pat, who eased his way, unnoticed, into the protecting shelter of the crowd of pupils.

A subdued class took its place at the bar, making private resolutions to devote itself to a life of ballet. The work began.

Madame, fired anew with memories of her own training at the Imperial School at St. Petersburg, was even stricter than usual. The jeweled stick darted mercilessly among the moving legs; and this was the moment an unlucky mother arrived at the studio to present her small daughter to Astafieva as a possible pupil.

The class watched curiously as a lady was shown into the studio. With her came a small, timid little girl.

"I am Astafieva, what do you want?" She frowned at the small, white card which had been handed to her. "What is this? Alice Marks, the Miniature Pavlova."

Everyone's attention was suddenly focused on the frail, dark-haired child. Her small, serious face was turned to Astafieva in grave-eyed wonder.

"Miniature Pavlova!" Astafieva jerked the card about angrily. "You mothers you are all the same." Her scorn broke lose. "You are idiots. Yes. You think because your daughter can stand on her toes and wobble she is a Pavlova. Yes? You don't know how long it takes to make a Pavlova, what work, what tears, what art. You don't know what it means . . . "

The little Alice Marks' big, dark eyes went on looking gravely at this beautiful, angry Russian lady, who wore such funny, shapeless clothes, but who had such perfect arms and legs.

Mrs. Marks beat an embarrassed retreat, taking Alice with her. (They were soon back again and Alice duly became a pupil.) Meanwhile Astafieva, who had just banished the future Alicia Markova from her studio, spent the rest of the class time delivering a long tirade against all dancing mothers.

"Not one of Madame's good days after all," Pat thought as he came out into the King's Road after the class.

As the subway rattled him across London he thought over what she had said. He wished with all his heart that he could have gone to the Imperial Ballet School in St. Petersburg. How wonderful it must be to give one's whole time to dancing, and not to be pulled about in all directions, trying to fit in dancing, acting, schooling and jobs as well.

"If I were in Russia, my training would be finished in three more years," he said to himself as he came up to the surface of the earth again.

He made his way through Russell Square to the Conti School in Great Ormond Street.

"Did you practice your elocution and voice production?" Italia Conti wanted to know.

Pat shook his head.

"Not very often. We didn't get time."

"Pat." She looked at him in despair. "You'll never get on in this profession unless you practice every day. But now you are back you must come to as many classes as you can to catch up."

Pat felt he had heard this conversation somewhere before.

He explained about *Peter Pan.*

"Yes, I know, dear. Mr. Boucicault told me he wanted

you for John again. I'll get in touch with your mother about the contract."

Peter Pan, dancing classes, acting classes. What about school lessons? Pat was very relieved when his parents agreed that it wasn't worth going back to his tutor for only the last two or three weeks of the term.

Rehearsals started.

At the New Theatre there was a joyful reunion of the *Peter Pan* family. There were not many changes. John, Michael, Wendy, and Mrs. Darling were all old friends. Most of the Lost Boys and Pirates had been in last year's company. A new Peter had joined them, however. Faith Celli was stepping, for the first time, into Peter Pan's brown leather jerkin and long, brown tights, with all the bewildering business of the part to learn.

This year, John faced Mr. Boucicault with all the confidence of a veteran actor who knew his part, while poor Peter, to whom it was all strange and new, became the target for the producer's temperament. The New Theatre rocked with shouts directed at the unhappy newcomer.

There were many tears before Faith was turned into a Peter that satisfied Mr. Boucicault's ideas. As before, though, once the curtain had gone up on the first night, the fiery temper went down, and they settled into their happy, backstage family life.

"Are you two coming down to tea?" Stella Patrick Campbell whispered to John and Michael in the wings as they waited for their entrance.

"Are you starting tea parties again?" Michael was delighted. "How lovely. Thank you very much."

"Come down in the second intermission, as usual," she told them.

Pat, however, had an idea of his own to pursue. During the intermission he tracked down the Kirby flying men to their lair below stage, and held a long and earnest conversation with Tom, the man who flew him.

"I don't mind doing it for you just once," said Tom as they went on stage for the Underground scene.

Pat felt he could hardly wait for the end of the play.

The curtain came down on the last scene. The theatre emptied. On stage, the men set up the Nursery Scene, ready for the evening show, and went off to their tea. The stage was deserted, until a soft padding of feet sounded on the boards, and a white figure appeared, coming through the Nursery door.

"Are you there?"

"Yes, I'm here." The whisper came from the dark shadows of the prompt corner. Tom appeared.

"Now, tell me exactly what you want." He clipped on the flying wire.

Pat, a ghostly looking figure in pajamas, stood in the unlighted nursery set.

"Will you take me straight up and down first." He placed his feet ready in the fifth position. Tom pulled on the rope and, as Pat went up in the air, his feet moved in a series of beautiful entrechats.

"I want to try some grands jetés now," he told Tom when the entrechat possibilities had been exhausted. "I'll run across, jump, and turn on landing."

Tom rapidly got the idea, and Pat had the unique sensation of leaping in the air and sailing across the stage in a series of perfect grands jetés. At least, they felt perfect.

"Here, young fellow, that's enough for now." Tom, out of breath, slackened off the wire.

"It was wonderful." Pat presented his back to be unhooked. "You see, on the wire I can do all the difficult things I've seen dancers do on the stage. Thank you very much, Tom." A package of cigarettes changed hands. It was the first of several more, as Tom good-naturedly allowed himself to be bribed, and Pat's flying ballet practice became a regular event after the matinee, until the stage manager, returning early from tea one day, found them at it. This put an end to Pat's idea.

"Well, it was wonderful while it lasted." Pat had to content himself with re-living the glorious feeling of floating through the air. He wondered how long it would be before his muscles would be trained, and strong enough to send him up in great leaps as he had seen other dancers do. What was the name of the famous Russian who jumped and flew like a bird? Pat leaned his elbow on his dressing-table and searched for the answer in his reflected face. Nijinsky! That was it. He could hear again Astafieva's clear voice telling him about this great artist.

"The most wonderful dancer of the age," she had said. "I have seen Nijinsky dance *Le Spectre de la Rose* with Karsavina." Astafieva had made the scene re-live for him. He could see the spectacular leap through the open window.

"Right across the stage he is carried, in a single movement. He appears to fly without effort. No other dancer could ever dance that role as Nijinsky did." Astafieva's eyes would light up as she spoke of it. "Yes, when Karsavina and Nijinsky first danced *Le Spectre de la Rose,* they took Paris by storm. Nothing like it had ever been seen before . . ." Her voice faded away into her memories of those glittering, pre-war days, when she too was dancing in Paris with the

Ballet Russe, and Pat, looking in his mirror, saw his own image blur and fade. Through his eyes seemed to appear those legendary dancing figures shining like distant flames lighting the way he was to follow. Could he follow? Would he ever be a dancer in his own right, or would he merely be an actor who danced?

Every instinct in him urged him to dance, but cold reason held him back, telling him that acting should be his career on the stage.

Which should he follow? Instinct or reason?

Which way did his future lie? To act? Or to dance?

18

Break

It was December, 1920. In a dressing-room at the Globe Theatre, London, Pat stood up to take a final look at himself in the mirrror, before going down to the stage for the last performance of *Fedora.* He saw a broad-shouldered, slim-hipped young man of sixteen, wearing the close-fitting uniform of a Russian page. Staring at his reflection, Pat thought how quickly the last two crowded years had passed, since the February vacation in Brighton his mother had made him take because he was run down. After that—what a kaleidoscope of memories he had! Dancing classes with Astafieva, and the supreme joy of hearing her praise him when he mastered his first 'tours en l'air'; acting classes with Miss

Conti, eagerly taking in all she could teach him; even shorthand and typing classes—to please his mother! Then there was the day when he walked proudly on to the stage of the Haymarket Theatre, to receive, from the hands of the great Ellen Terry herself, the British Empire Shakespeare Society's prize, which he had won in an elocution competition. And, of course, he remembered his third year in *Peter Pan,* when he realized, sadly, that he was getting too big to play John.

"Your call, please, Mr. Kay." The door rattled.

"Thank you."

"Mr. Kay" grinned at himself in the glass, and, as he turned away, he was already wondering what his next part would be.

He hadn't long to wait. Soon afterwards, Italia Conti sent for him.

"I want you to go for an audition, Pat." She churned over the tumbled papers on the desk. "Evelyn, where's that thing from the St. James's Theatre?"

"Do you mean this?" Evelyn produced a letter from a drawer.

"That's it." Italia, unwilling to admit that she needed glasses, held the paper at arm's length. "It's a play called *Threads.*"

Pat got the part and was called for rehearsal at the St. James's Theatre.

The theatre echoed to the sound of the modern, strident voices of 1920, and maybe the gentle ghost of Sir George Alexander lingered in the empty theatre watching his successors at work, and mourning silently for the good old days.

They had been rehearsing a week. *Threads* was beginning to take some sort of shape.

"What's the matter with you this morning?" the producer called up to Pat as he started on his lines. "Can't hear you."

"I'm sorry." Pat stepped up the pressure, but his voice was husky; he couldn't get the volume out.

"Have you got a sore throat?" the producer asked. "You've been sounding rather rough the last day or two."

"No, I haven't got a sore throat," Pat replied, and his voice sounded strangely hoarse to himself now. "I'm all right."

There was a startled giggle from those around him, for the last bit came out in a shrill squeak.

Pat blushed scarlet, and put his hand to his throat. What horrible disease was lurking there?

"Come here, boy." The producer beckoned him down to the footlights. "How old are you?"

"Sixteen." Pat, taking no more risks, whispered the answer.

The producer looked at the others and then back at Pat. "That's it," he said. "Voice breaking."

Pat had a great deal to think about as he left the theatre that day. This was to be a break in more ways than one. It was going to mean giving up his part in *Threads.* "Broken Threads," he said to himself smiling. It was also going to mean the end of his acting career for the time being.

"How long does it take for one's voice to finish breaking?" he asked his mother when he got home.

"It depends. It may take three months, six months, or even a year. Some take longer to settle than others." She shared his disappointment, understanding so well what he was feeling. After all these months of work and struggle, now, just as he was beginning to make a small success and be in demand by producers and managers, it was suddenly ended.

"By the time I can get jobs again, everyone will have forgotten me," Pat croaked gloomily. "I'll have to start all over again."

It was curious, he thought suddenly, how fate seemed to turn in a circle. It was from St. James's Theatre he had started out on his serious acting career, to follow Sir George Alexander's advice by joining the Conti School. Now, three years later, the same theatre had seen the end of it, anyway for the time being.

"I shan't go back to Conti's," he told his mother. "I mean, there's no point in going on with elocution and voice production with a cracked voice."

Mrs. Kay hid the sudden stab of disappointment his words gave her. She supposed he was right, and that it was unreasonable of her to have expected him to go on there. After all, he would go back to the stage later on, she told herself. He had worked too hard on it to throw it all away.

"You must do what you think best, dear," she told him gently. "At least you still have your dancing."

"Yes," said Pat slowly. "I still have my dancing." With that thought in mind he left her to wander out of the house and down the road, for the urge to be alone had come upon him.

He went down to the river and sat on the rails at the end of the park, just as he had done on his first day in London. That day had been a milestone in his life; this, he felt, was another. Almost five years had passed since he had first sat here looking down at the water. It had been summer then, and the sun had sparkled on its surface. He had sent his hopes and ambitions out on the moving current. What had he achieved in five years? The beginning of an acting career? Already it seemed to be finished.

Today the river was cold and brown in the dull winter light. Pat's eyes followed the flowing current. Had he really wanted to be an actor, he asked himself, or had he forced himself along that path to please his mother and father? Did he really want to take up his acting career again?

The wind rippled the surface of the water and the shadows moved and danced. As he watched them it seemed that the shadows in his heart lightened and lifted. Yes, he still had his dancing. More than that, he was now free to give his whole mind and body to it. No more would he be pulled in two directions, torn between acting and dancing, wondering which he should choose. His breaking voice had, for the present, made the decision for him. He could devote all his energy to dancing.

The thought sent the blood pulsing swiftly through his veins again. Hope and ambition went out once more on that swift current. He renewed his resolution to be someone who counted in the world.

The run of Pat Kay the actor had finished. The curtain was now to rise on Pat Kay the dancer.

19

The Russian Tradition

ONE AND TWO, three and four . . . " Madame's deep Russian voice chanted the time. "Keep your body straight, head up. One and two . . . " The long, jeweled stick tapped the floor. "Yes. That will do. Turn. Now on the other foot. One and two . . No!" The stick flashed out. "Keep your leg turned out. You—Jois, knee straight. Patté, stretch your foot more." Madame walked along the line of pupils working at the bar.

"All right," she clapped her hands. "In the center everyone."

The tall mirrors against the wall reflected the graceful figures moving to the insistent beat of the piano and Madame's clear voice.

Pliés, battements, ronds de jambe, arabesques, jetés, entrechats, fouettés. These things formed the whole pattern of Pat's life in the days that followed the end of his acting activities.

"Don't you get sick of doing nothing but dance?" Anthony, home for the Christmas holidays, sympathized over Pat's breaking voice.

"No, I don't," replied Pat, "I love it."

"Don't you miss the stage?" his young brother persisted.

"No, I don't think so," and now he came to think about

it, Pat realized that, already, he had left acting very far behind him.

"It'll be the first Christmas for a long time that you haven't been working." Mrs. Kay smiled, happy to have both her sons at home. How different they were, she thought. Anthony, very much the schoolboy, concerned with football and tennis and winning his colors. Pat, half boy, half man, had not yet found himself. He was still reaching out after his dream, the half-formed vision that had haunted him ever since he was a little boy, and still eluded him.

"Since I'm not working, let's have a party at Christmas," Pat was saying. "Let's ask lots of people. We haven't had any real family parties for ages . . . " He suddenly fell silent, remembering their parties in the old days, when Philip had been there to share them.

"I don't think we can, darling," Mrs. Kay reminded him gently. "You see, Father really can't stand much noise."

"Oh yes!" and Pat was moved to swift shame for he had forgotten about his father. Mr. Kay hadn't been very well for some time now.

"What's the matter with Father?" Anthony wanted to know.

"I'm afraid your father isn't as young as he was," Mrs. Kay explained. "He's not very strong these days, and the doctor says he must lead a very quiet life."

"How dreadful to be ill and getting old," thought Pat, and his bounding youth and vitality revolted against the idea of the creeping weight of years on his body. Would the time really come when his own strong legs became feeble and he could no longer command his muscles and know the joy of dancing? He chased the thought away.

"Yes," Mrs. Kay was saying, "the doctor thinks we should move to a quieter district."

"A new house! That'll be exciting," both the boys decided. "Where shall we go?" They spent the rest of the evening discussing places to live.

Mrs. Kay had not told them all that the doctor had said.

"He may last for many years yet," the doctor had told her, and she knew that meant he never would get better. Meanwhile he must be kept quiet and free from noise. The most she could hope for was to prolong his life by careful nursing.

So it came about that, early in 1921, once again the big vans stood outside 49 Bishops Mansions, while a team of men slowly emptied the house of its contents. This time, however, Pat was not going with them. The labels on his trunk read: King's Road, Chelsea.

"Goodby darling," his mother said, as she saw him into a cab. "We'll see you on Sunday, shan't we?"

"Yes, of course you will." He kissed her, and she sighed a little as she watched him being driven away. She hated to let him go, but she knew it was the only thing to do. She couldn't keep a high-spirited boy like her Pat in the sick-room atmosphere of a hushed house. She knew that all her patience and courage belonged now to her husband, and Pat must fend for himself for a while.

"After all, we shall see him quite often." She tried to console herself. "Hampstead isn't so far away from Chelsea." But she sighed again, for she knew that this break from home marked the real end of Pat's childhood. This sixteen-year-old son of hers, with his deepening, husky voice, was a man now, starting on his own independent life. Though the love and understanding between them would never be spoiled, he could never be her little boy again, running to her to be taken in her arms and comforted, or to share all the treasured, small things of everyday life with her, and her heart was sad, as all mothers' hearts are, for the young days that will never come back.

Pat was going to live with Astafieva. She kept a few rooms at the studios for resident pupils, and Pat, half pleased, half fearful at the prospect, was going to be one of them. What would it be like living in daily contact with that vivid, difficult, turbulent personality? He stared out of the cab windows with unseeing eyes, thinking what a wonderful teacher Madame was and wondering what she really thought of his dancing.

It was a question he had often asked himself. For three and a half years now he had been going to her classes. People had told him that her favorite pupils were the ones whose legs carried the most bruises. If that was true, Madame must love him very much, for his legs were always black and blue from that flashing stick. Does she really think I have talent? Pat asked himself. She had never shown that she did, or singled him out for special encouragement in any way. As far as he could see she had always treated him like all her other pupils. He came for his lesson; if he worked well she smiled and said "good"; if he worked badly, there was the stick to make another bruise on his legs. That was as it should be, but there were the days when he wanted something more, the days when he felt discouraged, and wondered if he was really going to get anywhere. "Is it enough to want to dance and to work hard?" he asked himself in his black moments of doubt. "Do I really have the talent to go to the top?"

This question was becoming more and more insistent. He wished again that he knew what Astafieva really thought of his work. She would never tell him if he asked her. Now, however, though he did not yet realize it, he was slowly to discover the answer for himself.

They were a small, happy family, that handful of resident pupils in the studio in the King's Road. Astafieva created about her the warm, Russian atmosphere of her own lively temperament, and Pat, ever sensitive to his surroundings, adapted himself swiftly to this new way of living and loved it. He ate strange Russian dishes, he learned Russian words, he absorbed the traditions of the Russian ballet.

Best moments of all, he found, were the evenings, when work was over for the day and the big studios were empty and silent. The door of Madame's sitting-room stood open, and her clear voice would call to them to come in.

It was warm and bright in this room with the thick curtains drawn, shutting out the gray London winter. In here was Russia. The firelight leaped on silk shawls that splashed bright color across the chairs. It shone on the gold and blue of a Russian ikon, and on the polished curves of the steaming samovar that stood ready on the table. It glittered among the photographs, ornaments, and souvenirs crowding the furniture. Every corner of that room was stamped with the vivid personality of its owner, and in the pool of light from the tall, shaded lamp, there she was, Madame herself, as Pat was always to remember that well-loved figure—her black hair swathed in the folds of a colored bandeau, the ropes of pearls around her neck gleaming milky white against the ivory of her skin. Those beautiful hands with long, polished nails; the inevitable cigarette; the quick, mischievous smile and the sparkle in her dark eyes as she welcomed them in.

They sat around the fire drinking tea the Russian way, in tall glasses. The smoke from Madame's cigarette curled up in slow, blue-gray shapes, and the photographs seemed to smile down on the circle of young faces. It was very still and very peaceful.

"Who is that?" Pat's attention was caught one evening by the fading picture of a dancer, a man in a curious looking costume of leaves—or were they petals?

"That, Patté, is the great Nijinsky." Astafieva watched his face as she told him. "He is photographed there in his costume for the *Spectre de la Rose.*"

Pat started, and looked again. *Le Spectre de la Rose,* that almost legendary dream ballet created by Nijinsky and Karsavina. So this was what the great dancer actually looked like. He studied the photograph more closely, and saw a man of middle height, thick set, with a strong neck, and powerful looking legs. So this was Vaslav Nijinsky! How different he was from what Pat had imagined.

"Ah Patté! No photograph can show you Nijinsky as he was." Astafieva had seen the disappointment in his face. "A picture, it is a dead thing. Only those who have been lucky enough to see Nijinsky dance can know what he really was. Nijinsky the man, he is nothing, he is shy, dull, he has nothing to say, you are disappointed, but Nijinsky the artist, let him put on his costume and dance for you and he is transformed, as though another spirit, the spirit of his role, had entered his body and taken possession of him. That is the genius of Nijinsky. I know, I tell you, I have been on the stage with him, I have seen this happen with my own eyes."

"You have danced on the same stage as Nijinsky," Pat repeated slowly, and looking at her, he envied her memories.

"Is he dead?" one of the girls wanted to know.

"No. He is alive. If you can call it that. How shall I say it?" Her hands moved in a tiny, broken gesture. "He is ill."

"He is very old I suppose."

"He is not too old to dance," said Madame sadly. "That is the tragedy. It is his mind that is ill." Her fingers tapped the side of her head. "Something here has broken. Everything has been tried to cure him." Her hands fluttered helplessly on to her lap. "Now, we can only pray that a great artist may be given back to the world again."

They stared in silent awe at the photograph that had caught one fleeting moment of his life and recorded forever the great dancer as he was in all his beauty and strength.

"Who is that?" One of the girls noticed another photograph nearby. "It looks as though it was taken a very long time ago." She studied the picture of a young, slender girl in a classical, white tutu.

"It is very old!" Astafieva's merry laugh drove out the brooding shadow of Nijinsky's tragedy. "That was me! It was taken at St. Petersburg, when I graduated."

"Oh dear, I am sorry!" The girl blushed. "I thought it was old because it's faded."

"It has traveled about a great deal," said Astafieva with her mischievous smile. "I like to have it with me to remind me that I too was once young and beautiful."

"How did you become a dancer?" they asked her. "Did your father and mother dance?"

"No." She shook her head. "I was the only one in the family. It was my idea alone."

"I suppose you were very good at dancing right from the start?"

"No. Just the opposite. My master did not like me at all. I was ugly and I was thin, and I was always crying." She laughed at the memory. "Mr. Pichot lost his temper with me and said I would never be a dancer, but still I wanted to go on. When I was eight, I was old enough to be taken to the Imperial Ballet School in St. Petersburg. Once a year all the professors, directors, and physicians assemble to choose their new pupils. From all over Russia the children come, hoping to be accepted. It makes no difference if you are the child of rich parents, or come from a poor peasant's home, if they think you will make a dancer they will take you, and train you. The year I went, there were only seven vacancies, and in the big hall there were three hundred children assembled. My parents thought they were wasting their time, bringing me, so thin and so ugly. We were lined up and examined by the doctors. We were questioned by stern looking men, we were made to walk, to run . . . "

"And you were chosen?" They couldn't bear the suspense.

"Yes. I was lucky. I was chosen." She laughed gaily. "You should have seen my parents' faces, their surprise that their ugly little daughter had been accepted as a pupil in the great Imperial Ballet School. As for me, I was the happiest person in the world. I joined the school and put on my uniform, a pink dress. All the new pupils wear pink. Later on you have a gray dress, and then, if you pass all your exams, a white dress. You are a very important person in the school when you have a white dress."

"Then you did nothing but dancing?"

"Of course not, we were educated too. We studied languages, literature, music, history, everything."

"Did you get vacations?"

"Yes. We were allowed home for Easter and Christmas, and for a vacation in the summer. Not very long though for we mustn't get out of training. After five or six years we might, perhaps, be allowed to see a Ballet at the Marynsky Theatre, by standing in a crowd scene at the back of the stage or walking across, but never more, for nobody may dance in the Imperial Theatre until the training is finished. Then the dancer may graduate into the corps de ballet."

"Did you still live at the school after you graduated?"

"No. We were allowed to go back home, but we still belonged to the Imperial Theatre. I enjoyed this new life." She glanced up at her photograph. "Do you know people said I had changed and become quite beautiful. I can't think why for I was still so thin, I weighed only eighty-four pounds, and my waist," she spread out her hands, "it measured only sixteen and a half inches. But my parents were proud of me again." Her black eyes sparkled. "Admirers sent me flowers and presents, there were invitations to dinners and balls. How gay it all was, but always there was work as well, exercises and practice, for a dancer can never rest."

"Why did you ever leave the theatre?" they asked her.

"Ah!" she smiled at them. "I fell in love. But it didn't work out, and we were divorced. I thought my life was finished," she went on. "I could never go back to the Imperial Theatre now."

"Why not?"

"Because I divorced my husband."

"What has that got to do with your dancing?"

"The Emperor was very strict. Divorce was a scandal in those days. It was not permitted for dancers to have any scandal attached to their name. No, the Imperial Theatre was closed to me forever. What was I to do? My parents had died. I had no money. How was I to earn my living, I who had only been trained to dance? Friends helped me. They were so good to me. Then, one day, I met Serge Diaghileff. He knew me from the old days at the Marynsky. He had often seen me dance, and he asked me to come now and join his company, the Ballet Russe. They had their headquarters at Monte Carlo. There I went, to start once again to dance." She stared into the fire, re-living those days. "Serge Diaghileff had collected in his company some of the finest artists ever trained by the Imperial Schools: Nijinsky, Karsavina, Tchernicheva, Lopokova, Fokine." The mighty names rolled out. "Pavlova too had been with them, but she had left to form her own company. The Ballet Russe under Diaghileff toured all the capitals of Europe, and everywhere, success. It was like the old days at St. Petersburg come back again. What triumphs. It would have gone on, too, but war came." Her face grew sad. "It was 1914. Revolution broke out. The Emperor was driven from his throne. The Bolshevik peasants came to power and ruled the country."

"What happened to Diaghileff and the Ballet Russe?"

"We were in Europe, cut off from our country. We had to survive as best we could. Poor Serge, he did what he could to keep his dancers together during four years of war. Poor big Serge. How he suffered to keep the ballet alive. How we all suffered. He had spent his own fortune and his friends' money; all that he could borrow or beg. He was penniless, but somehow he kept going with a few dancers, giving seasons where he could."

"You left him?"

"Yes," she smiled sadly. "I had to, for even a dancer must eat. I came to London and started my school."

"What does Diaghileff do now?" It was Pat who asked.

"Since the war finished he is building up the Ballet Russe once more."

"Don't you want to go back to him?"

"No!" She looked up swiftly. "It is too late. Serge will find new dancers for his company. My work is here, in my school." She smiled at them. "The future of the ballet now must be in the hands of you young people."

Pat looked at her, hardly daring to ask the question that lay so close to his heart.

"Can we ever become as great artists as those who trained in the Imperial Schools?"

She was silent, looking at this boy, whose hopes and ambitions were shining in his eyes.

"Why not, Patté?" she said softly. "If you go on working hard, everything is possible." And her eyes held for him both a challenge and a promise.

20

Serge Diaghileff

"Go on working hard," Madame had said, and her implied encouragement had sent Pat's ambition soaring.

"One day," he announced in all the pride of his sixteen years, "I too shall dance with the Diaghileff Ballet."

Madame had not laughed at him.

"You are right, Patté," she told him. "You work for only the highest prize. Diaghileff's Ballet Russe is the finest artistic organization in Europe today."

Could Madame's far-seeing eyes look into the future then and see him fulfill his ambition? She said nothing, and for Pat himself the Ballet Russe remained a distant goal, as he practiced and struggled and fought his way to achieve technical perfection.

As a dancer he was still concerned with technique, with the mastery of each classical movement, and the control of each muscle in his body. The artist in him had not yet been stirred into life. The full awakening of the soul of the dancer was to come later.

Meanwhile, the winter days lengthened into spring and summer. Madame flung open the tall windows of her studio, letting in the warm sunshine and letting out the cascading music of her classes, to mingle with the hum of passing traffic.

It was not only ballet music that joined the noisy bustle of the King's Road. Often the syncopated beat of a foxtrot, or a throbbing tango went out through those open windows, as dancing couples gyrated over the studio floor. Under Madame's skilled training young and unknown names were growing up to fame as exhibition dancers.

Madame was tireless. She held special classes also for acrobatic dancing. Sometimes Pat was allowed to watch a training that brought all his old delight in acrobatics flooding back. He felt rather guilty about this, and would creep away on his own into a deserted corner afterwards to try out some of the things he had seen.

Madame caught him one day.

"What are you doing?" she screamed at him. "You, a classical dancer, standing on your hands? The good God gave you feet to dance." The storm raged in a torrent of broken English and Russian, but Pat's heart leaped in him for joy, for every angry word showed how much his dancing mattered to her.

"Go away," she raged at him. "Go and watch real dancing. Here . . ." she fumbled in the sagging pocket of her jacket . . ."you go to the ballet tonight. Go and watch Karsavina dance, and put these other ideas out of your head."

Pat, clutching the coin she had given him, happily joined the second-balcony line that was forming outside the Coliseum on that warm summer evening.

"Hello!" He was greeted by the "regulars." Many were young dancers and ballet pupils like himself. There were others, of indeterminate occupation. They were a curious collection of penniless young enthusiasts, united in a fervent worship of the Ballet.

The whole cult of the dance was taken very seriously.

Pat, who went to see every ballet he could, had spent many hours in second-balcony lines engaged in hot argument over the rival merits of Karsavina and Pavlova, or the music of Tchaikowsky versus that of Stravinsky.

They were noisy, young and enthusiastic, and wherever ballet was performed its followers would be found, faithfully lining up to fill the second balcony and shout their praise or disapproval.

It was in this high perch that Pat had spent enchanted hours. From the second balcony of the Prince's Theatre he had seen the tiny figure of Pavlova floating across the great stage, and the spell of the beauty she wove about her had reached up even there, and caught him in it. Pavlova was something out of this world.

Now the doors of the Coliseum were swung open. Coins rattled down on the wooden ledge of the box office, and the noisy, cheerful crowd went surging up the stairs to scramble for the best places.

The theatre was filling. Somewhere behind the heavy curtain that hid the stage the great Russian ballerina was preparing to enchant them with the beauty of her art.

Pat remembered his first experience of such beauty, the night he had seen Astafieva dance on this very stage. As long as he lived he would remember the deep emotion her dancing had aroused in him, as though she had opened a door, showing him all the loveliness that lay in an enchanted world the other side of it. He could still feel the driving urge that had made him determined to learn from Astafieva herself and none else. How blindly right he had been.

Since then, he had seen much dancing, but only two dancers could move him in the same way. The divine Pavlova, and Karsavina. How often he had seen Karsavina already, when she made those all-too-brief appearances at the Coliseum. He never lost the thrill of seeing the houselights fade, feeling his heart beat faster to know that she was there, poised in the wings, waiting.

The voices around him hushed and died. The moment had come again.

To Pat, Karsavina was a flame. She moved with a faultless beauty as swift and sure as a bird in flight. What a technique, what a style, born of those long years of training in the Imperial School. Through the music he seemed to hear Astafieva's deep voice telling the story of those years of training, the flowering of talent, and the young Karsavina's triumph in Paris; the immortal partnership with Nijinsky; the pair of them dancing their way to the glittering pinnacle of success in the Ballet Russe. But behind them there stood always the figure of the man who had made their triumph possible, who had brought the Russian Ballet to Europe; the man who, to Pat, was still a mysterious, shadowy figure, an unknown power—Serge Diaghileff.

"Bravo! Bravo!" A sallow young woman sitting next to Pat came noisily to life as the curtain came down for the intermission. "Did you see those fouettés?" she shouted at him through the racket of the balcony's approval. "Perfect. Never seen her do them better. Bravo!"

But Pat, who was thinking into the great dancer's past, said:

"How I wish I could have seen her dance with Nijinsky."

"Nijinsky?" The name brought into view a pale young man in a yellow pullover on the other side of the sallow girl. "People exaggerate the artistry of Nijinsky." He leaned across to argue. "What else could he do but leap? Now the real dancer to see is Massine."

"Nonsense." The sallow girl shook her lanky brown hair. "Massine hasn't half the technique."

"I saw Massine dance here, with the Diaghileff Ballet . . ." the young man began.

"Diaghileff?" A voice interrupted from the row behind. "Is it true that Diaghileff is bringing his Ballet Russe to London for a season?"

Pat twisted around, ears and senses alert.

"Yes, it is true." A man's voice shouted along the row. "They are coming here in September."

The distant voice broadcast the information around the balcony. "Diaghileff is planning to stage a revival of the *Sleeping Princess*."

"What, all of it?"

"Yes, it's a full-length ballet. Never been seen outside Russia."

"And Diaghileff is going to do it in London?"

"So I heard."

Pat sat in a dream as the young voices chattered on around him. Diaghileff coming to London with his whole company. He would see these fabulous Russian dancers at last. Perhaps he would see the great man himself. He was filled with an intense curiosity and desire to see this Serge Diaghileff. The Ballet Russe were coming to London. His whole body tingled with excitement.

"Do you think it's true?" he pestered Astafieva afterwards.

"Patté, darling. How should I know what big Serge is doing?" she laughed at him. "You will see soon enough when the time comes if it is true."

He did.

Towards the middle of September paragraphs in the

papers carried the news that the Russian Ballet had arrived in London to start rehearsing for the *Sleeping Princess.*

There was great excitement among Astafieva's pupils.

"Does it give the date of the opening night?"

A whole bunch of them had gathered around a newspaper just before the morning class was due to begin.

"No. It only says they'll be at the Alhambra. Sh! Here comes Madame."

The newspaper was hurriedly bundled out of sight.

Astafieva was smiling as she came in. This was a good sign.

"Today, my children," she told them gaily, "you must work extra well. We are expecting a very important visitor. Yes." Her eyes sparkled mischievously. "You have seen in the papers that the Ballet Russe is here in London. Well, they need extra dancers to take part in the *Sleeping Princess* and they are coming here to find them."

"Who is coming?" Pat had to ask.

Astafieva looked at him a moment.

"Serge Diaghileff is coming himself," she told him.

Diaghileff looking for extra dancers! Diaghileff coming to the studio to choose them himself!

They looked at each other and a sudden fever of excitement went pulsing through them all. They were to have a chance to be chosen to dance with the Russian Ballet.

"He may come today, or he may come tomorrow," Madame went on. "He told me he was not sure. Meanwhile we must be ready to show him what we can do."

Work started. How hard it was to concentrate on the preliminary exercises, ronds de jambe and battements. The bell rang.

"Pay attention, will you." Madame's stick tapped the floor angrily. "Think what you are doing."

It was all right; the bell was a false alarm.

"One and two and three and four . . . " Madame's voice dominated the class, demanding concentration.

Will he come today? Pat's legs moved mechanically. What did he look like, this great man who owned a ballet? Madame had spoken of "Big Serge," so he must be tall.

"Patté! Patté!" The stick smacked on his legs. "Pay attention. Tempo. Two and three and four . . . "

The bell rang again. Pat's heart raced. This must be he.

No. He relaxed again.

One and two . . . Would he come today . . . ? Three and four . . . The question beat in his brain Would he come? Would he really see Serge Diaghileff today? There was the bell again. Another false alarm, and a stab of disappointment. Surely the studio bell never rang so often on other mornings.

"All right. That will do." Madame released them from the bar. "Into the center. Petit adagio."

"Perhaps he'll come now." Pat watched the big hands of the clock move around.

"Grand adagio . . . allegro." It was after 12:30 now. The class would soon be finished. He hadn't come after all. Wait! Was that the bell? No. It would be for tommorrow.

"Go back and do that enchainement again," Madame called out to two of the girls; and at that moment came a loud knock, as though someone had struck the door with a heavy stick. It opened. In the doorway stood a group of people.

No need to ask who was the big man in the black fur-collared overcoat, who led the way into the studio, swinging a gold-mounted cane.

The girls swept down in a curtsey; the boys bowed low.

"Serge!" Astafieva greeted him with open arms.

Serge Diaghileff stooped to kiss her affectionately, and the studio was suddenly filled with strong Russian voices.

The pupils, forgotten for the moment, effaced themselves against the wall, watching, listening, and wondering who were the other three people who accompanied Diaghileff. It was only later they were to learn that the slim young man was his secretary, Boris Kochno. No ordinary secretary this, but an intellectual and a poet. The tall, suave man who swept his arms in wide, graceful gestures when he spoke, was Serge Grigorieff, a trained dancer from the Imperial School, and now Diaghileff's right-hand man, and stage manager. Beside him stood a beautiful and distinguished-looking lady, whose poise and classic features bore the unmistakable stamp of the dancer. This was Grigorieff's lovely and talented wife, Lubov Tchernicheva, première danseuse of the Ballet Russe.

They stood in a group talking and laughing with Astafieva. Pat, however, had eyes for the central figure alone. It was he who dominated the room. Everything about Serge Diaghileff was unusual. His powerful physique, that massive head with its noble breadth of forehead, the curious white streak in his dark hair, the monocle that gave him such a look of arrogant power. He had a short, wide nose, typically Russian, a sensual mouth under a small dark mustache. He had the heavy jaw of a fighter, and, by contrast, the white, sensitive hands of a man of culture and taste. He was laughing as he spoke with Astafieva. They spoke in Russian; his voice had a lazy, caressing quality that was strangely attractive. Pat wondered what they were saying.

They moved down to the end of the studio. Chairs were quickly brought.

Madame called out her pupils. In ones, twos, and threes they danced. Pat, waiting with the other two boys in the class for their turn, saw Diaghileff's cane swing up and point to a small serious-faced girl who had just finished her dance. He said something in Russian, and Madame beckoned to the child to come up.

"This is Alice Marks," they heard Madame say in English. "She is only twelve." She went on to speak in Russian, and Pat wondered whether she was telling him of the first day that Alice Marks had appeared in the studio; the awful scene when her mother had introduced the "Miniature Pavlova," and an enraged Astafieva had slammed the door on them. That had not been the end of it though, for nothing was going to stop Alice Marks from dancing. The offending cards had been torn up, and back she had come, this time to be admitted to Madame's classes, and to prove herself one of the most promising pupils. Now, here she was singled out by Diaghileff himself. What an unerring eye for talent he had. Could they have looked into the future, they would have seen that in two short years, this little girl, standing now so gravely before him, would join the ranks of his Ballet Russe as the youngest dancer ever to be engaged.

Diaghileff was leaning forward, smiling at his future Alicia Markova. They couldn't hear what he was saying, but they saw her curtsey and run to join the others.

The dancing went on, watched by those expert eyes. Grigorieff's calm and wise. Tchernicheva's dark and critical. Diaghileff's inscrutable, half-hidden behind that glinting monocle. From time to time he leaned over and spoke to his companions, and the stick singled out the lucky ones.

"Patté," Madame called him out at last. "We want to see you dance alone. You do *Humoresque*."

Alone! His chance had come. His heart was thumping fast as he moved out to take his place. This dance was the only one he knew. Madame had arranged it for him to the famous music of Dvořák. It was a dance they had both seen executed by Volinin when he had appeared with Pavlova at the Prince's Theatre.

The piano began, and Pat in all the innocence and audacity of youth, now danced this elegant and difficult solo before these most expert and critical judges.

Diaghileff was smiling as Pat finished, a big, lazy smile that showed a glint of gold in his white teeth. Was he impressed by Pat's performance or by the sheer audacity of a boy attempting so difficult a dance?

Madame signed to Pat to approach. Diaghileff rose and stood looking down at this young dancer.

"How old are you?" His voice had a soft burr as he spoke in English.

"I am seventeen." Pat was staring, fascinated at the great man, now so close to him.

"One day you will dance." Diaghileff's hand rested on Pat's head and for a moment he looked full at him. What a curious, compelling power shone in his eyes, as though there was a light behind them, and he could see right into one's innermost thoughts. "Now you shall come and watch my dancers."

He turned away swiftly. The moment was over. Pat went to join the others, shaking with emotion. It was all finished, he had been picked. He was going to dance with the Ballet Russe in the *Sleeping Princess*.

21

Rehearsals of the "Sleeping Princess"

THE ALHAMBRA THEATRE, Leicester Square, seethed with life, and the young dancer Pat Kay was caught up and lost in the turmoil of preparation. Yet how few of them could realize the full scope of this gigantic undertaking in which they had a part.

Nearly thirty years had passed since the *Sleeping Princess* had been first performed on the stage of the Marynsky Theatre, St. Petersburg. Now, Diaghileff was staging a sumptuous revival of this single, three-hour ballet in the pure classical tradition, a ballet that had never been seen in its entirety outside Russia.

The *Sleeping Princess* was to be awakened and brought to Europe to herald the triumphant return to the pre-war glories of the Ballet Russe. Diaghileff had assembled around himself the most famous team of artists of the day.

The Russian painter Bakst had designed the costumes and seven great scenes—a riot of pageantry and color. It was to be his last and perhaps his greatest work for Diaghileff. In Stravinsky's master hands lay the score of Tschaikovsky's beautiful music, especially written for this ballet. Sergeyeff, trained in the classical tradition, handled the choreography that had been first evolved by Petipa, the great Maître de Ballet of the Imperial School.

This superb, classical ballet had been created to revolve about one person, the central, dazzling figure of Aurora, the Sleeping Princess. For Diaghileff, however, one ballerina was not enough, and, for his production, no less than three top-ranking ballerinas were brought in especially to share the honors of this great role. Olga Spessiva and Lubov Egorova had arrived in London. Soon Vera Trefilova was to join them.

Behind these queens of the dance gathered Diaghileff's own famous dancers of his Ballet Russe, and around them swarmed the crowd of extras, and walkers-on, especially engaged for the production. Altogether a cast of two hundred people collected in the Alhambra Theatre. The opening date was fixed for November 2nd.

All day and frequently all night, the work went on. Russian voices dominated the turmoil as Diaghileff's key men took over. Chief Machinist Koristoff, a tall Russian with a startling red beard, took charge of an army of English stage hands, carpenters, and property men. In the labyrinth of passages and rooms at the back, Vassily reigned over his kingdom of wardrobe assistants, sewing machines, ironing boards, and costumes. The whole building echoed to the sound of musical instruments as the orchestra rehearsed under Stravinsky.

For Pat, a tiny cog in this vast machinery, the first days were spent in the cold, bare rehearsal room with a crowd of other extras learning steps under the stern eye of the choreographer, Sergeyeff. He was a short, spare man with a grim expression and a fixed purpose, perfection, even for so straightforward a matter as walking across the stage.

Occasionally during rehearsal the door would be unexpectedly flung open and the big figure of Diaghileff would be there, watching. His visits always spurred them on to greater efforts, and even when he had gone the feeling of his watching presence remained.

This one powerful man was the central focus of all the activity that went on during those chaotic days. Everyone in the theatre was aware of him. He had an uncanny way of making each of them feel that they were working for him alone.

One day he came into the rehearsal room to speak to Sergeyeff. Pat was called out.

"Try him," said Diaghileff in English, and Pat discovered that he had been chosen to dance in a waltz.

"We need four male dancers for the waltz," Sergeyeff explained afterwards. "Only three can be spared from the company."

Pat didn't need to be told what an honor it was to be singled out for this. His only fear was that he should not prove good enough.

"Don't worry so much, Pat." His waltz partner Hilda Bewicke calmed him down as he muddled his steps. "I tell you what, we'll stay behind after rehearsal and go over it again by ourselves."

How comforting she was and how hard Pat worked at his little dance.

Soon they were all ready to come out of the preparatory school of the rehearsal rooms to work in big groups on the stage itself. How vast and bleak it was on the first evening they assembled on that empty stage. Down in the cold, gloomy auditorium a group of people sat. The broad shoulders of Big Serge were easy to pick out. Beside him sat the dapper, trim Leon Bakst. Nearby was the familiar grim figure of Sergeyeff, and with them two dancers wrapped in furs. On the side of the stage by the piano Pat recognized the tall, graceful stage manager, Grigorieff. He was talking to a woman wrapped in a long, dark cloak.

Pat wondered who she was. She half turned and he saw her face, a curious face, pale and rather heavy with big, slanting eyes and an untidy mop of yellow hair.

Pat nudged one of the extras near him. "Who's that?"

"It's Bronislava Nijinska. She is helping Sergeyeff with the choreography."

"So that is the sister of the famous Nijinsky." Pat, looking at her, felt a pang of cold disappointment. She wasn't beautiful, she didn't even look like a classical dancer—or did she? Nijinska had suddenly flung her cloak back. She was moving, demonstrating something to Grigorieff. Training and style showed in every line.

A voice of authority called out suddenly from the auditorium. Grigorieff hurried to receive Diaghileff's instructions. Rehearsal began. They were to feel the difference now, for the master himself had taken over. It was tiring work. Every few minutes the dancers were interrupted.

"Wait," Diaghileff would call up, and they waited while he consulted with Sergeyeff, or Stravinsky. Others would join in, there would be argument and gestures, while everyone on stage hung about getting cold and bored.

"All right, do it again with the quicker tempo." Diaghileff would get up, and stride towards the footlights. There he stood, his long overcoat thrown over his shoulders, his head curiously tilted as he watched.

"No." He clapped his hands. Back they went over it again, once, twice or as many as twenty times until it was artistically right.

"That will do. Rest." Tired dancers moved away to the

wings forming little whispering groups. Diaghileff went back to his seat.

It was time for Aurora's pas seul. The whispering groups fell silent, and all turned to watch as the principal figure came on to the stage. In her plain, practice costume, Olga Spessiva looked little different from the other danseuses. She stood, waiting for her music, looking, with her frail beauty, like a slender, ivory statuette. Then she danced. That graceful, delicate body had muscles of steel. What a style, and what a technique! Her dancing was the finished, perfect product of the Russian School.

"Bravo!" The elite in the auditorium called out as her dance came to an end. Spessiva, smiling, made a mock curtsey to them and ran off. The corps de ballet moved in once more. The work went on. For Pat, the ordeal of the waltz passed off without special incident. The ordeal of the mazurka was still to come. This dance was in the finale of the ballet. Pat felt happy enough as long as he was hidden in the back row. The moment arrived however, when the long line of dancers circled around the stage. This meant coming across the front in full view of those critical eyes.

"Patrickieff!" Diaghileff suddenly called out. "Awful! Patrickieff, what are you doing?"

Pat suddenly registered the fact that he was hearing his own name. Diaghileff had Russianized it for him.

"Patrickieff!" the deep voice called out again. "Tempo! Tempo!" and his stick beat the floor.

"That's done it," Pat decided as the mazurka finished. "They'll throw me out. He said I was awful."

The rehearsal was nearly over. Tired and miserable, Pat waited to be dismissed and told not to come again. He saw the short, spare figure of Sergeyeff hurrying through the pass-door on to the stage. He stooped short as he caught sight of Pat.

"Ah!" he said. "I was looking for you."

The tone of his voice made Pat feel cold all over.

"We want you to stay behind after the rehearsal," Sergeyeff told him. "You are to go through the mazurka again." He passed on quickly.

"That is all for today, thank you." Dimly, Pat heard the stage manager's voice dismissing the company. "Rehearsal tomorrow at the same time." The dancers drifted away. Pat was left alone on the stage.

"Now then." Sergeyeff suddenly reappeared. "We will work at this step." Patiently, clearly, he showed Pat how it was to be fitted into the music.

The small solitary figure went dancing around the empty stage. Pat, intent on his work, did not see a silent, dark silhouette standing in the shadows at the back of the theatre.

"That will do for now." Sergeyeff released him at last. From the depths of the theatre came the soft sound of a door closing.

"How late you are, my poor Patté," Astafieva called out as she heard him come past her door. "Why do you come in after all the others?"

"I had to stay behind and practice." Pat felt rather guilty having to admit this. There was a pause, and then:

"Come in!" Astafieva called out sharply. "What did you say? They made you stay behind?"

"Yes." Pat stood in the doorway and bowed his head, waiting for a deluge of reproach. "I was in the mazurka and Diaghileff called out in front of everyone that I was awful."

"And he kept you afterwards?"

"Yes."

"But that is wonderful!" Astafieva beamed. "Wonderful, Patté."

Pat gave up all hope of understanding these people.

"Don't you see, you stupid boy." She laughed at him. "It means they take an interest in your dancing. Do you think they would waste their time to give you extra practice unless they thought you were worth it?"

"Oh!" This was a new idea to Pat. Perhaps Astafieva was right. He thought things over. Diaghileff had picked him out of the studio class here; he had picked him out at rehearsal to take part in the waltz; and now he had been picked out to stay behind and rehearse.

"Does it really mean that he thinks I have talent as a dancer?" Pat asked himself. "Will I get the chance perhaps to join the company of the Ballet Russe permanently?"

The hope formed in his mind and grew there.

22

First Night

DIAGHILEFF HAD set his publicity agents to work and seen to it that everyone was talking about this fabulous ballet that was in preparation behind the closed doors of the

Alhambra. As a result, the restless, post-war London of 1921 with its short skirts and long cigarette holders, with its convulsive Charleston and strident jazz, scrambled for first-night seats at a romantic, classical ballet. The advance sale boomed.

The days passed swiftly to the evening of November 2nd. Outside the Alhambra, ballet enthusiasts had been lining up since the early hours for second-balcony seats. The stage door was besieged all day with messengers, errand boys, pages, workroom girls. Boxes, packages, letters, telegrams, last-minute costumes and wigs, presents, flowers, and laurel wreaths poured through. Inside, the stairs and corridors seethed with hurrying figures. Away in silent hotel bedrooms, principal dancers rested with their legs up. At all costs they must be calm and relaxed before their exacting work tonight.

As dusk drew over the city someone turned a switch and the dark front of the theatre was suddenly a blaze of light, flashing the *Sleeping Princess* into the darkening sky, and cheering the patient balcony below. While they waited in the cold, a group of men were dining at the Savoy. Diaghileff, Stravinsky, Bakst, Boris Kochno and several more sat down to caviar and smoked salmon, and drank champagne to the success of the Princess. Diaghileff was pale, there were deep shadows under his eyes. He had spent most of the previous night in the theatre, working without rest to insure the perfect working of scenery and lighting. The strain of the weeks of preparation showed in the tired lines of his face, and his friends were aware of the tense undercurrent of anxiety, of nerves strung to fever pitch.

At the theatre the fashionable public were beginning to arrive. A Diaghileff first night never failed to attract a brilliant audience. Leicester Square was jammed with cars and taxis moving slowly up to the lighted entrance. A crowd gathered to watch, and in the brilliant, flower-decked foyer, critics and faithful first-nighters jostled with the rich and the successful, the well born and the talented.

The second-balcony door opened and the patient line was suddenly brought to life and swallowed up through the dingy side entrance.

"Overture and beginners please." The call boys hurried around. Dressing-room doors opened and down the stairs they thronged, to crowd in the wings waiting and whispering, listening to the hum of that unseen audience on the other side of the great velvet curtains.

It was nearly time. The theatre was packed. Only one box still remained empty. Heads were turned as the door at the back of it opened. There was a gleam of white shirt front as a big man in immaculate evening dress came through, followed by a group of others. He took his place in the center of the box: his monocle flashed as he looked around. There was a stir; people nudged each other.

"That's Serge Diaghileff who has just come in."

The lights dimmed, and the talk died. The conductor raised his baton and the glorious music of Tschaikovsky filled the house. Smoothly the heavy curtain rose on a scene of breathtaking grandeur: the Palace of the King and Queen at the birth of Aurora; soaring columns reaching for the sky, the vast sweep of marble staircases curving majestically into distant space, on the white steps of which were ranged tier upon tier of motionless, living figures, the scarlet and gold Negro guards of the King's Household.

To the music of a march the stage filled with the glittering figures of the King's Court. It was a wealth of color and pageantry centering around the golden cradle of the baby Princess. Here came the fairies with their gifts. Ballerinas in white tutus decorated with the emblems of their power, and accompanied by their pages, carried out a series of brilliant pas de deux.

The dark-eyed Tchernicheva, who had come to Astafieva's studio on the famous day of Diaghileff's visit, was now a lovely vision in the white and scarlet costume of the Mountain Ash Fairy.

The Cherry Blossom Fairy, a graceful fair-haired dancer who hid an English birth under her Russian name, Sokolova, brought her gift to the cradle.

Nijinska, transformed into the Humming Bird Fairy, took the stage, dancing with a style and power that evoked memories of her famous brother.

The Pine Tree Fairy, the Song Bird Fairy, they all came, and after them the sinister entrance of the wicked fairy Carabosse, whose ugly, wrinkled make-up covered the faded beauty of an aging dancer named Carlotta Brianza. She had been specially brought from Russia for this part. Perhaps as she danced her wicked role this night, her thoughts went back to an evening at the Marynsky Theatre nearly thirty years before in 1892 when the curtain had gone up on the first performance of the new ballet the *Sleeping Princess* and the applause had rung out for the young and lovely ballerina, Carlotta Brianza, who had danced the role of Aurora before the Czar himself and all the elite of the old Russian nobility.

A last brilliant dance from the belated Lilac Fairy, Lopokova, and the curtain came down at the end of the scene.

In her dressing-room the Aurora of 1921 waited for her

entrance. To Olga Spessiva had fallen the honor of dancing the great role on the first night. The mirror reflected a radiant vision in a deep rose-colored tutu, with a bodice laced with gold. On her head she wore a wonderful pale gold wig. The dresser placed a shawl around her delicate shoulders.

On stage a sweating team of stage-hands swept away the palace to replace it by the Royal Gardens. There was some delay in getting the heavy scenery shifted into place. Friendly applause, however, greeted the rustic celebrations of Aurora's sixteenth birthday. A circle of peasants in red and green costumes were dancing about the stage. Out of the romping music grew the celebrated village waltz. Four couples detached themselves from the throng to hold the attention for a brief few minutes.

"Well done, Pat," Hilda Bewicke whispered to him as they whirled to a finish, and the new dancer who appeared in the program as "Patrickieff" smiled back at her. At least that bit was successfully over. He was hot and shaking as they passed into the shadows of the wings, crowded with courtiers standing ready for their entrance. There waited Aurora herself, glorious in white, red, and gold.

Pat slowly made his way near to gaze at the loveliness of Olga Spessiva. As the moment of her first entrance neared, she slid the shawl from her shoulders. Pat saw his opportunity. He hurried forward and took it. She gave him a fleeting smile over her shoulder as she moved away. He saw her bow her head and cross herself three times. The next moment, Aurora floated into the brilliant lights.

Pat stood hugging the soft, scented shawl as he watched her. He was still there, waiting, when she came off. Greatly daring, he put the shawl over her shoulders, but was too over-awed to find the words to tell her how her dancing had moved him.

The applause from the audience was warm and heartening. All was going well until the scene shifting broke down badly. The mechanism that worked the Lilac Fairy's spell became jammed. The curtain remained down for long, tedious minutes while stage-hands worked frantically to get it right and dancers stood about nervy and worried. The audience grew restive.

After this, the whole complicated stage machinery seemed to be thrown out of gear. Another long delay preceded the rise of the curtain on the Prince's Hunting Scene. The evening was not halfway through yet. There was still the Awakening. In a room deep in shadow, a single shaft of light shone on the golden-haired princess, asleep on a gigantic canopied bed, veiled by a monstrous web guarded by two enormous spiders.

They were running nearly an hour late now. At last the curtain came up on the final brilliant spectacle—the scene of Aurora's Wedding.

Vast colonnades, open to the sky, curved into the distance. Spiral pillars of white and gold, entwined with flowers, made a fairy-like setting of space and beauty. It was perhaps one of the most successful sets that Bakst ever designed.

The action of the story was finished, and the scene was given over to a spectacular ball, led by Aurora and Prince Charming.

There was a series of brilliant divertissements.

The last mazurka. "Tempo. Tempo, Patrickieff!" Pat could almost hear Diaghileff's voice calling out as he danced across the stage. Swiftly came the grand finale, and the audience were cheering and calling out. The balcony was wild with enthusiasm. The unlucky delays had already been forgotten and forgiven, it seemed, in their crescendo of clapping.

The curtain came down at last, and for the company there was the sudden bubbling up of relief and excitement that the first night was safely over.

Back to the dressing-rooms they went while autograph hunters massed at the stage door, and privileged visitors pushed their way in to find their friends. Parties started up, champagne corks popped. There was laughter and gaiety backstage for success seemed to smile at them. Life was wonderful, or so thought a very tired young man, letting himself into the studio in the King's Road in the early hours of the morning.

23

Goodby

THE PRINCESS had been rapturously received by the first-night public, but the critics, bored by the unfortunate delays, had not been kind in the papers next day. Although the scene-changing machinery was in perfect order by the end of the week, the poor Princess never recovered from her bad start.

More than that, the public could not get used to the idea of the same full-length ballet night after night. They lost interest. Box office receipts began to fall off.

"Another bad house tonight, I hear." A group of extras were standing in the wings.

"Expect it'll pick up a bit over Christmas," another was saying.

"Hope so. I can't afford to be out of work yet."

"Excuse me."

They moved aside at the sound of a soft voice. The pale, golden wig of Aurora shone among the colored costumes of the courtiers. How small and frail Olga Spessiva looked among the men.

She smiled as she saw Pat standing near.

"My little boy with the shawl," she said as she handed it to him.

Since that first night he had never missed his self-appointed task of holding Spessiva's shawl. Always he was there in the wings to watch her performance. He watched Trefilova too and Egorova when the danced Aurora in their turn, but Spessiva remained always his first love.

What a lot Pat learned, as he stood in the wings night after night, watching the great dancers. He studied the men; and seeing the performance of the leading dancers Vladimiroff, Wilzac, Idzikowsky, and Woizikowsky made him realize how little he himself knew. He also realized for the first time what art and skill lay in a male partner's role. He had never given much thought to this before, but now he began to see for himself how important it was, and how a partner could make or mar a ballerina's performance. He watched Vladimiroff as Prince Charming partnering Aurora. How beautifully he handled her, always effacing himself, timing every move to blend with hers. How easily he lifted her without sign of strain. He made her look as light as a bird in his arms. How gently he controlled her descent, to land her softly on one pointed toe. Pat's imagination leaped forward to the day when he too would partner a ballerina.

As he placed the shawl over Spessiva's beautiful shoulders again he longed suddenly to put his hands around that tiny waist and raise her shoulder high. How angry she would be.

"Thank you, Patrickieff." She smiled at him and he blushed, glad that she could not read his thoughts. She turned away to speak to Vladimiroff. How Pat wished he could understand their language. The few words he had picked up from Astafieva were soon drowned and lost in this sea of Russian that surrounded him.

A group of the regular corps de ballet of Diaghileff's company were gathering near him now. He gazed at them wistfully, wishing he could be one of them. He used to watch them practice on the side of the stage, or exercise in the rehearsal room. They worked in little groups on their own. At first Pat had hoped he might be allowed to join them, but he soon realized that this was not to happen. A barrier seemed to stand between him and them. Was it language only? Or was it the pride of artists who knew they belonged to the finest ballet company in Europe, a team that had no place for untried strangers.

"They will recognize me one day." His ambition beat strongly in him, and he turned again to the stage to watch Lopokova and Idzikowsky dance the Bluebird, one of the most thrilling and difficult pas de deux ever created. The Bluebird called for brilliance, strength, and an impeccable technique.

Pat forgot his disappointment as he stood now absorbed by the beauty of the music and the brilliance of the performance. Slowly, however, he became aware of a presence near him. There was a scent of almond oil, the weight of a hand on his shoulder. He looked around and his heart beat faster, for Serge Diaghileff was looking down at him.

"And when are you going to dance the Bluebird?" There was a smile in his eyes.

"When you want me to." There was no hesitation about the reply. The hand on his shoulder tightened as though this was the answer Diaghileff wanted to hear.

It was the first time he had taken any notice of Pat since the rehearsal. Both of them, however, were to remember this little incident which had its strange sequel three years later. The night Anton Dolin danced the Bluebird for the first time in London he received a laurel wreath and on the card, in Diaghileff's own hand was written, "When will you dance the Bluebird? 1921-1924." The amazing man had not forgotten.

Did he foresee that night already in 1921 as he stood beside Pat in the wings of the Alhambra? The dance finished. Pat watched him move away to speak to someone else. What thoughts and plans went on in that powerful head? Was it possible that he would want Pat to join his company after this? The secret hope throbbed with quick life.

Whatever plans Diaghileff might have had, nothing could come of them, for all too soon it became obvious to everyone that the days of the Princess were numbered. She would never run six months. By the new year it was doubtful if she would last three. In the middle of January the notices went up on the boards, announcing that the run of the *Sleeping Princess* would finish in two weeks.

The great experiment, though artistically successful, was a disastrous financial failure. Diaghileff had run up huge debts to put on this ballet. When the curtain came down for the last time, the pack of creditors closed in on their prey. The *Sleeping Princess* was to be torn apart.

The cast disbanded. Principals returned to Russia. The extras disappeared into the oblivion from which they had come. Diaghileff, hounded and worried by debts, fought to keep his own company together. Many of them, fearing to be out of work, left him to join Massine at Covent Garden.

Most tragic of all, Bakst's glorious scenery and costumes, which had cost thousands of dollars, and for which there was no money, had to be abandoned, to fall into the hands of creditors and be lost or irretrievably destroyed.

Diaghileff gathered the faithful remnants of his company around him and prepared to leave. Their destination was the south of France, the sunshine of Monte Carlo, headquarters of the Ballet Russe.

On a dark February morning in 1922 a very sad-hearted young man watched the long boat train pull out of Victoria Station, carrying away Diaghileff and his dancers. With it seemed to go all Pat's hopes and dreams. He was left with a sense of emptiness and desolation.

Would he ever see Spessiva dance again? Would he watch Idzikowsky and Lopokova in the Bluebird? Would he ever see Diaghileff, that strange and powerful man who could build a dancer's career, and create a ballet that was a piece of sheer, living beauty?

Pat felt like a child who had been shown a glimpse of fairyland, a place full of beautiful, dancing figures who had beckoned him and lured him in to dance with them in their enchanted world, and now, he had been pushed back, the door had been slammed, and he was left on the outside, alone.

"If only I could have gone with them," he thought in the desperation of his loneliness, and he suddenly wanted sympathy. He wanted to talk to someone. Not Astafieva, she had too much courage, and Pat felt at this moment he had none at all.

He took the subway for Hampstead.

His mother welcomed him home. He realized guiltily how little he had seen of her since he had been caught up in the glamorous spell of the *Sleeping Princess*. Hurried visits, scribbled postcards, rare telephone calls. She had been to some of the rehearsals, and of course she had seen the finished performance, but their moments together had been rare. He had grown out of talking everything over with her. Since living on his own he had gotten used to keeping things to himself and working out his own problems. Could she understand now what he was feeling, inside? Could she know without his having to put it into words? It seemed she could and she did understand.

How good it was to be with her again. She looked tired and worn though. Her husband's failing health was taking all her strength. He had his good days when he went out. There were more frequently his bad times when he stayed in the house, or remained in bed.

"Go into the sitting-room and talk to him, darling, he'll be so pleased."

Pat, seeing his father in the armchair by the fire, thought how old he had become, and was touched with deep pity that he could not express. He felt embarrassed, and talked of trivial things, wishing there could be between his father and himself that sure, deep understanding that had always existed with his mother. He knew that it was his own "demon of the dance" that had brought this about. His father, puzzled and bewildered, could never get used to the idea of having a son who was a professional dancer. His mother had always understood, and believed in his dancing with all her heart. How lucky he was to have such a wonderful mother.

He came away from her comforted and reassured, able once more to face the future. She gave him back his courage to match Astafieva's indomitable spirit, and to listen also to the quiet voice that spoke deep inside telling him that, as a dancer, he was not yet ready to take his place in a company like the Ballet Russe.

Pat shook off his depression, faced up to reality, and went back to Astafieva's studio to work.

24

Creation

THE MUSIC of Beethoven's *Pastoral Symphony* poured out of the battered phonograph perched precariously on a chair. Sprawling on the floor beside it, Pat listened in a rapt stillness until the last chords, changing abruptly into the ugly hiss of a scraping needle, broke the enchantment.

The young people in the room stirred and came to life.

"All right, I'll take it off." Molly Grosvenor reached out and lifted the arm.

"Now, let's listen to something more modern." Her friend Poppœa Vanda began sorting over the pile of records.

"No, put on something by Tchaikovsky." Pat struggled into a sitting position.

"The greatest composer who ever wrote for the ballet." Poppœa waved a record around to emphasize the point. "Let's see what we've got of his."

"I've found something," Molly Grosvenor interrupted suddenly. "We must listen to this." She put on Borodin's *Prince Igor.*

Impossible to lie still and relaxed to the music of the Polovtsian dances. The stirring music seemed to bring wild Cossacks right into the room. Pat's eyes glittered as he listened. He felt his muscles grow taut for action.

In the middle of it the door opened. It was Astafieva.

"I hear *Prince Igor,* I come in," she whispered. "No! No! Don't move." But Pat had already jumped up to find a chair for her. When the record was over she stayed on, talking with them.

"Patté, you are growing up." She sent him a mischievous smile.

Pat wasn't sure he approved of this.

"I am grown up," he said in his deepest man's voice. "I shall be eighteen next month."

"You are growing up as a dancer as well as a man," she told him.

"How do you mean?"

She looked around the room, at the table strewn with records and books, at his friends, Poppœa Vanda and Molly Grosvenor.

"You reach out beyond the studio and the bar," she said. "Until now, you think that to be a dancer is to have technique, that once you have learned all the steps, to do them perfectly, there is nothing more to learn. Now I see that since you have been with Diaghileff you have other ideas. You have seen that to be a great dancer you must have more than a fine technique, you must have—how shall I say it?—a dancer's soul. So, Patté, I am happy that nowadays you think about things, you listen to great music. You see how you grow up? You read books too!" She picked up a stray volume lying on a chair. *History of the Ballet.*

"That's mine," said Molly Grosvenor. "I brought it along to lend Pat."

"That reminds me," put in Poppœa. "We brought along something else for you too, Pat. We've got a new record that you must listen to. It's Rimski-Korsakov's *Hymn to the Sun.*"

"Who's playing?" asked Pat.

"Isolde Menges," Poppeœa told him as she wound up the phonograph.

It was strange and beautiful music. There was a pagan, primitive spirit in it that matched the mood of modern life. Pat listened to it, thinking over what Madame had said to him.

It was true, he was now reaching out beyond the studio and the mere perfection of technique. What did he hope to reach? What did he want? The questions floated formlessly in his mind on the surging tide of the music. As he listened, strange emotions moved in him. He was suddenly linked across the years to his own childhood. He felt himself a little boy once more, listening to the music of his mother's piano, and unbearably moved by it. There rose in him again the urge to put into movement all the feelings that the music aroused. It was an urge that had lain dormant, forgotten for years under the strict discipline of his training.

"What a lovely violinist she is." Poppœa's voice brought

Pat to the reality of his surroundings again. The record was over.

"Do you think I could borrow that record, Poppœa?" he asked. "I'd like to play it over again."

"You can keep it," said Poppœa, swiftly generous. "We brought it for you." She turned away to ask Madame for news of Diaghileff. It was four months since the *Sleeping Princess* had finished.

"Poor Serge, he is having a hard time," Madame told them. "He is still in Monte Carlo. The *Sleeping Princess* ruined him. He has no money to put on a Paris season. This summer he does only Ballets Chantés in the Monte Carlo Opera House." She shook her head, grieving for the troubles of Big Serge.

"I wonder if there is a future for ballets with singing?" said Molly Grosvenor thoughtfully.

"Why not?" Poppœa pushed aside the records and leaned over the table ready for a discussion. "They have ballets in opera; why not singing in ballet?"

"But surely it can never be justified, artistically."

The argument started up. Pat joined in, Madame left them to it, and the three of them went on arguing and talking late into the night.

After Poppœa and Molly Grosvenor had gone, however, and Pat was alone in his room, he picked up the record of the *Hymn to the Sun,* and stood a long time staring down at the shining black surface, while an idea slowly formed in his mind.

Pat loved these evenings in his room when friends came in and sat listening to fine music or talking, discussing books and articles they had read, or ballets they had seen. Sometimes when Madame joined them she would start telling them stories of Russia and the great dancers, till Pat, unable to sit still another minute, would jump up and dance himself. Or, if the mood was on him, he would get a pair of old toe shoes from the dressing-room and dance the solos from the *Sleeping Princess* while Madame sang.

It was an atmosphere of youth and hope, of preparation for things to come.

But while Pat's life stretched ahead, full of promise and a world waited to be conquered, another life had nearly run its course.

In the quiet house in Hampstead the flame of this life was burning low. It flickered and went out.

The news of his father's death sent Pat hurrying to his mother's side. Sharing her sorrow, he wished again that he and his father had been able to understand each other better. He was old enough now to realize what a bitter disappointment it must have been to his father to have a son who danced. It was so far removed from everything he had been brought up to value. Pat loved his father for the sincere and simple man he was; a true sportsman of the old school. How empty his life must have been these last few years, living in London, cut off from everything that had made his life worth living. "And all because of me," Pat realized. The family had come to London because of his dancing. His father had made that sacrifice so that his son should be able to do something he neither understood nor really approved of, and the sorrow welled up in Pat afresh for all the things that were gone and could never be brought back, and because his father had died too soon without seeing his son fulfill his destiny. "But you shall be proud of me yet," Pat vowed to the spirit of his father, and it came to him that he was now the head of the family, the oldest son. He would take care of his mother and Anthony now, he was eighteen and a man. As though she knew what he was thinking, his mother smiled at him through her tears. He found her hand and held it fast in his, and perhaps at that moment, the thought of Philip came to them both and sorrow tore anew at their hearts.

This was the final break-up of the family home. The house in Hampstead was given up, the furniture stored. Mrs. Kay, drained of strength after months of devoted nursing, went to the country to stay with relatives. Pat took a small studio of his own in Molly Grosvenor's house and went back to his dancing, back to the world that he belonged to now, and loved.

Astafieva had been right when she told him he was growing up. A change was coming over his work. He began to understand what he was doing and to be aware of the possibilities of his body. Now, when he danced before the big mirrors in the studio, he was not looking to see if a leg was properly turned out or a foot correctly placed, he was watching the lines that his body could create, discovering for himself what was beautiful and what was ugly.

He tried experiments on his own before the mirror, with different positions and steps. The idea that had formed in his mind grew insistent and one evening in his own studio he brought out the phonograph.

In the twilight of an autumn dusk the music of the *Hymn to the Sun* flooded the small room. Once, twice the record played through before the crouching figure beside the phonograph came to life and began to move. He stretched up his arms and let his body respond to the music that swept through him.

The mirrors reflected a dancing figure glimmering in the

half-light, and as Pat danced the blood seemed to course through his veins like fire. The record finished. Now, to remember those movements, to try them again. The urge to create was on him and the hours fled by.

When Pat finally stumbled into his bedroom and flung himself down, his strength was spent, but in his exhaustion was a deep content that he had not known before.

"Patté. Patté. That is careless work." Astafieva's stick landed heavily on his legs in class next morning. "What have you been doing that you work so badly?" She came close to him, peering at his pale face and the dark shadows under his eyes. "Ah! Late nights. You sit talking to your friends Poppœa and Molly Grosvenor." There followed the usual lecture about dancers getting plenty of sleep.

"You go to bed early tonight. I don't want to see a face like that in my class tomorrow," was Madame's parting remark to Pat that evening as she herself went out to dinner. A few minutes later, as she passed some people coming up the stairs, he heard her say loudly, "And you, don't you keep him up late again."

"What's the matter with Madame?" His friends came into the dressing-room to see if he was ready. "What's all this about keeping you up late?"

"We didn't," added Molly Grosvenor. "We left you on your own last night because you said you didn't want to come out."

"I worked badly in class today," said Pat, "and she thinks I look tired."

"Oh!" Poppœa investigated. "She's right, Pat. You look awful. What have you been up to?"

"Nothing." Pat was unwilling to part with his secret.

"Do you think you had better not come to the theatre

with us tonight?" Molly Grosvenor was looking at him with a puzzled frown.

"Why, Pat!" Poppœa burst out laughing. "You do look guilty. I believe you'd forgotten all about it."

"No, I hadn't," said Pat. "But . . . "

"But what?"

"What is all this mystery?" They closed in and got the story out of him.

Pat expected them to laugh at him but it was just the opposite.

"I think it's thrilling." Poppœa was enthusiastic. "You must let us see that you've done."

"Let's go back home right now," added Molly Grosvenor.

"What about the theatre?" Pat hedged.

"Never mind about that," Poppœa retorted. "This is important."

Back in his own studio Pat danced and they treated his work with the sincerity and seriousness that all true creative effort commands. He warmed to their encouragement and interest. They praised and criticized; suggestions were made, new ideas tried out.

The *Hymn to the Sun* began to take shape. Pat's confidence in himself grew, and the day arrived when Astafieva came upon him rehearsing his new dance in her Chelsea studio.

"So." She looked at him intently. "You too, you will create a dance?"

"You must see it, Madame," Poppœa told her.

"But it's not finished," Pat protested.

"No matter, let me see what you have done." Madame's interest was aroused.

The studio was cleared. The other students collected to watch. Pat danced to his first audience.

There was light and excitement in Astafieva's eyes as she watched.

"Bravo, Patté." She clapped her hands as he finished. "You begin to dance, really to dance." There was pride and delight in her voice. This young plant she had tended for so long was grown into a bud ready to open into full flower. He was ready now to receive all the great treasures of knowledge that she could give him. He was no longer just a talented pupil. He had become a fellow artist. The soul of the dancer was stirring into life.

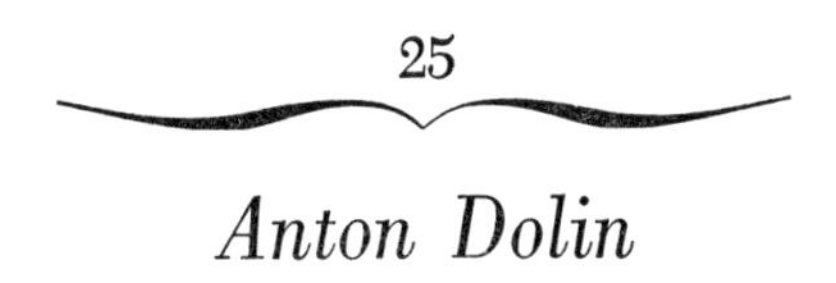

25

Anton Dolin

THE SUMMER had come around again. It was the summer of 1923. Over a year of solid work lay behind Pat. Long weeks of routine daily classes, his technique growing under Madame's patient, brilliant teaching. Side by side with this, his creative dancing had developed by watching others and by trying new experiments himself. Helped and encouraged by those who surrounded him and believed in his future, the artist in him grew.

The *Hymn to the Sun* was completed. Hardened and shaped in the fire of criticism, the first rough dance, sketched out on the autumn evening nearly a year ago, had been hammered and polished into a finished, shining thing.

Out of the welter of experiments another dance had grown to completion. *Dance Russe* gave expression to the young dancer's love and admiration for the great people who had passed on their art to him. Perhaps as he danced it he was aware also of a shadowy figure in the background of his mind, a man with a curious white streak in his hair, and an enigmatic expression in his eyes. Did the future lie in this direction? Or was the *Dance Russe* a tribute to past things?

Diaghileff had once described Pat as the "little boy with brown eyes." There was nothing of the little boy left now. The last shreds of childhood had fallen from him during this past year. In the place of the uncertain boy who had fought and struggled blindly along the path of his destiny stood a young man, strong in the quiet confidence of his own growing powers. At nearly nineteen Pat was slim and muscular. The years of his training had molded his body to the supple grace of a dancer. There was love and pride in the eyes of his "dancing mother" Astafieva as she saw this "child" of hers, grown into all the vigor and beauty of a young male dancer. Soon he would be ready to leave her, to make his own career in the world. Could either of them guess how soon?

Certainly neither of them could guess that it was the finger of fate pressing the studio bell during class one morning in June. The finger in question belonged to a Mr. Charguine. His card carried the information that he was an impresario.

Madame returned from the interview with the light of battle in her eyes.

"I have just promised that we shall put on a dancing exhibition." She looked around the class, pausing to give the full effect to her news. "We dance in the Albert Hall on June 26th."

There was a stunned silence.

"The Albert Hall!" They looked at each other. "And by the end of the month."

"It appears that another dancing performance was booked for that date," Madame explained, "but something happened and they cannot do it, so I am asked if I will provide an entertainment, and I say 'yes,' " she told them airily. "There is not much time so we must work quickly."

From that moment the Albert Hall loomed largely in everybody's life. The school had, of course, given displays and taken part in charity shows many times before. From the existing repertoire Madame began to compile the program. This, however, was no hired hall and piano effort; this was to be a dancing exhibition on a grand scale.

"We shall have an orchestra," Madame announced. "A large orchestra. The costumes we shall rent or have made." She scratched about on the littered table in her room looking for the first draft of the program.

"Patté!" she called him in. "Come here and see the dances you have to do." She waved the paper at him.

Pat looked down the list and saw the familiar items, extracts from classical repertoire, one or two modern arrangements and mime. For him it was the usual group work and partnering, with a short solo or two among the divertissements. He handed back the list.

"I should like to have a dance of my own to do," he said.

"But you have a solo in the divertissement."

"I mean an item of my own," Pat explained. "I would

like to dance the *Hymn to the Sun* and the *Dance Russe*."

Astafieva looked up at him swiftly.

"I arranged the program," she said. "If I had wanted to put them in, I would have done so."

Her voice and words sent a sudden tide of revolt surging up in Pat. Why shouldn't he be allowed to do his dances? Madame herself had said they were good. As though a voice within him was telling him that his whole future depended on it, his determination hardened.

"Why shouldn't I dance them?" he argued.

Unfortunately Astafieva was accustomed to having her own way in these matters.

"If you dance a solo it will be something that I choose." She spoke in a hard, clear voice and her words were the spark that sent Pat's Irish temper raging up inside him.

"I will not dance what you choose," he shouted at her suddenly. "I will do my own dances."

"You will dance what I say." She banged her fist down on the table.

"I will do my own numbers." Both temper and temperament had taken possession of him like a demon, and he no longer cared what he said. "I will not be dictated to by you," he screamed at her. "I shall dance what I think is best for me and if not I shan't take part at all in your exhibition."

"You will learn to do what you are told," Madame screamed back. "Get out and go into the studio for your rehearsal."

He went, slamming the door.

Pat's temper cooled but his determination remained. He was now resolved to have his own way about this. Rehearsals became a battleground. Pat, still possessed by his demon, either sulked or screamed. A deep instinct in him was driving him on to fight for his right to do his own dances. He was long past caring what he said.

In his cooler moments he half expected Madame to turn him out of the school altogether or at least to forbid him to speak like that to her, but strangely enough she did neither. She put up with his temper. She seemed, even, to understand. She let him scream and give full voice to his feelings, but she was too obstinate and her own fiery, independent nature was not ready to give in. The whole school was awed by the din of battle.

"I tell you I will not have my pupils telling me what they will or will not dance," Madame yelled at him across the studio.

"Why not? It is we who dance." Pat worked into a blind rage, knocked himself against the wall, fell over and rolled on the floor, refusing to get up.

"That's right. You knock your head. It is good for you. You knock some sense in it maybe."

Madame's full, rich laugh suddenly went ringing out. Pat sat up, purged of rage, and feeling rather foolish. Her laugh had brought him to his senses.

"Come on, Patté, it is finished now; you work," she told him.

Pat got up and they looked at each other. He knew without being told, that it was truly over; he had made a fool of himself and he had won. The *Hymn to the Sun* and the *Dance Russe* would be put on the program.

No more was said. The rehearsals went on quietly, and Pat, as though he wanted to make up for his display of temperament, went enthusiastically to work to help in any way he could. Night after night he stayed up late helping to copy out extra parts for the orchestra.

"I don't know what I should do without you all." Madame came into her room one evening to find half a dozen of them sitting around a table strewn with musical scores. "Patté, you are a great help to me." She came and leaned over him, a paper in her hand. "Would you look at this now and see that I have spelled these names as they should be." She put the final draft of the program before him. "Mon Dieu, these English names, they are so difficult."

Pat smiled as he took the paper. He looked down the list. There were *Dance Russe* and *Hymn to the Sun* with his own name staring back at him.

"I don't think Pat Kay will look very good in print," he said thoughtfully. "It doesn't sound like a dancer, does it?"

"We can put Patrickieff if you like, as you had for the *Sleeping Princess?*" Madame suggested.

Pat considered this. It was, in fact, the first time he had really thought about his name.

"No, I don't think Patrickieff is right," he said, frowning. "I must find something else. Yes," he warmed to the idea. "I'll disguise myself under a completely new name. It'll be fun, I'll mystify all my friends."

"You do what you like with your name," Madame told him, "but this list must go to the printers in the morning, early."

"What sort of a name do you want, Pat?" one of the others asked him.

"I don't know exactly. Something very Russian but not too difficult." He went over to the shelf and found a volume of Tchekov.

"Let's see if we can get any ideas out of here." He

flipped over the pages. The name Anton stared up at him from the printed page.

"Anton," he said out loud. "I like that. What do you think?"

The jury around the table stopped copying band parts and decided that they liked it too.

"Now for something to go with it," said Pat, but Tchekov could only suggest long and complicated surnames.

"There's nothing here under five syllables." Pat pushed the book aside. "Nobody would remember them, let alone spell them." He appealed to Madame. "Haven't you any simple surnames in Russia?"

The answer to this question was a knock on the door. Mr. Charguine the impresario had arrived to see how the preparations for the show were getting on. He was rapidly drawn into the discussion.

"So you want a name to go with Anton." He looked at Pat. "What about Dolin?" he suggested at length.

"Dolin?" Pat frowned. "That doesn't sound very Russian."

"But it is," replied Mr. Charguine. "Anton Dolin is a very good Russian name."

"Yes, and it is a good name for the stage." Madame was becoming quite enthusiastic about the idea. "I can hear the public call out 'Bravo Dolin.' "

"Anton Dolin." Pat tried it out rather doubtfully. "I suppose it does sound foreign. Anyway it's easy to spell."

"Anton Dolin." He wrote it down with a flourish.

"Anton Dolin," people read in the printed program as they took their places in the Albert Hall on June 26th, and in a dressing-room at the back Anton Dolin was putting on his ballet shoes and getting ready amid the turmoil that is an inescapable part of a one-night show.

Out in front the boxes and seats were far from full. A dancing exhibition was not a powerful magnet for the mass of the public, and the Albert Hall itself, vast, gloomy and circular, was not the ideal setting in which to stage ballet.

A bored sprinkling of men and women with notebooks occupied seats labeled "Press." To them, this was just another routine job.

The performance began.

It was a pleasant entertainment. Madame's pupils in their classical white tutus looked young and lovely and they danced with precision and style, the hallmark of their famous teacher. The audience appreciated it and clapped politely. A short modern piece by six of the students was well received and then came the moment for which one small group of people in the audience was anxiously waiting.

A stirring Russian rhythm that sent the blood tingling brought a whirling, leaping figure on to the stage. The fire and vigor of his dance stirred the imagination of those who saw him. Even the critics sat up and looked interested. That bounding dancer on the stage seemed to embody the very spirit of Russia.

Applause broke out, spontaneous and full.

"Who is that young man?" people asked each other as he ran back to take his bow. The program told them it was Anton Dolin.

"I don't seem to have heard that name before," they told each other. Which was hardly surprising.

"What a remarkable agility."

"He hardly touches the ground."

Comments like these reached the ears of Mrs. Kay who sat with a group of her friends. They looked at each other and smiled triumphantly. It was a proud moment.

The display continued. As it drew near the end of the show people began to say:

"What comes next?" Programs rustled again.

"*Hymn to the Sun*," they read. "Anton Dolin."

"That was the young man who did the *Dance Russe* so well." A sense of eager anticipation surged through the audience.

They were not prepared, however, for what they did see. The dramatic opening bars of Rimski-Korsakov's music echoed through the hall. A magnificent young pagan appeared on the stage. From that first moment he held his audience. He carried them with him, in the fiery, primitive dance of a pagan praying to the sun to pour down its warmth on his body. There was drama and power in every line of that splendid body, which lifted the dance right above the level of the rest.

The audience realized that they were witnessing something dramatically outstanding. The applause was thunderous.

As the whole performance came to an end and the dancers lined up for their bows, the shouts rang out for "Dolin."

"Bravo Dolin!"

The stage was suddenly filled with a riot of flowers, but at Dolin's feet were green laurel wreaths, the first he had won.

"Bravo Dolin!"

To the echo of applause the dancer Anton Dolin was born.

It was an unforgettable moment.

26

The Critics

"No, I'm not going to bed, we're going to celebrate." Pat's room was crowded with young people, and his mother, who wouldn't go to bed either, was installed in the best armchair, while Astafieva who wouldn't even sit down, paced about restlessly, talking, reliving every moment of the evening. Champagne was fetched, toasts were drunk, and a sense of feverish gaiety laid hold of them. Pat hung up his laurel wreaths.

"I can't rest now till I've seen the papers," he declared, and they prepared for an all-night vigil.

When the champagne ran out they drank coffee, and sat about in quieter mood smoking and talking, until the dawn chorus of the London birds heralded a new day, and the early streaks of dawn lighting the sky sent young people hurrying out into the deserted streets in pursuit of first editions.

Before long newspapers covered the furniture and floor of Pat's studio, and from the printed columns still damp from the press, there arose a unanimous chorus of praise:

"Last night at the Albert Hall . . . was a young man in advance of many of the established stars of the day."

"Dolin was as light as a feather, as graceful as a fawn."

"He combined the most marvelous agility with a true dramatic instinct."

"I, for one, believe that Dolin, ere long, will be proclaimed the rival and successor of Nijinsky."

"Pat! What wonderful notices." They all congratulated him.

"Every one of them is good."

"You've won over all the critics. There's not a single adverse notice."

Pat, dazed with happiness, tasted the first rewards of his long, hard work. How worthwhile it all seemed now, and how he loved all these loyal friends who had helped him, and were as pleased about his success as if it were their own.

There was one person, though, who mattered above all those who surrounded him. He sent a special look to his mother. Her happiness and pride in him glowed in her eyes. She was sharing this great moment to the full.

"Will you keep the name Anton Dolin?" someone was asking him.

"Of course I will; it's a lucky name." Superstition ran strong in Pat's Irish veins. "Anton Dolin brought me success."

So, the name that was chosen for fun, to mystify his friends, remained. It had brought him luck. It was to bring him something else as well. The echoes of his success were to reach out beyond the shores of England and across the Channel.

A letter arrived for Astafieva. It bore a Paris postmark, and bold foreign handwriting sprawled across the envelope.

"Patté." She called him excitedly. "Patté, come here."

"What is it?"

"I have a letter from Serge Diaghileff." She waved the

paper about. "He has seen in the papers that there is a new Russian dancer Anton Dolin. He writes to me to know who it is." Her dark eyes were sparkling with mischievous excitement. "Big Serge thinks he knows every dancer of note in Europe. He is curious about this Anton Dolin."

Pat's heart beat fast as he listened.

"I shall write and tell him," Astafieva went on. "I shall say that Anton Dolin is the little boy Patrickieff he engaged for the *Sleeping Princess*."

Like a door opening before him Pat saw the opportunity he had been wanting. He had aroused Diaghileff's interest.

"Will you ask him then, for an audition?" he begged her. "Ask him to see me dance again."

She did. She sent Pat's photograph as well.

The letter reached Diaghileff just before he left Paris.

What did he think as he sat with Astafieva's letter in his hand and the photograph of the "little boy with brown eyes" on the table in front of him?

Did it carry his thoughts back over the eighteen months that had passed since the *Sleeping Princess* had sent the Ballet Russe down to the very rock bottom of their fortunes?

A year of scraping and struggling to keep the company alive had followed that disaster. Diaghileff had held on. Then, six months ago, it began to look as though the tide of ill-luck was turning at last. The Princess of Monaco had graciously extended her patronage and the company now bore the offical title of the "Ballet Russe de Monte Carlo." No empty honor this, but a title that carried with it the privilege of presenting each year a three-month season of their own ballets in the Royal Opera House.

Monte Carlo had become more than their headquarters, it had become their home.

Already this year 1923 had opened with a successful season there, bringing in enough money to enable Diaghileff to launch a Paris season. June and July had seen the Ballet Russe dancing to well-filled houses at the Théâtre Gaieté Lyrique in Paris. Now the company were having a six weeks' holiday, and after it, a tour planned for the autumn would take them to Belgium and Switzerland.

The Ballet Russe were very much alive again, and recovering rapidly, but the team was not complete. The place of the leading male dancer remained empty. Nijinsky had gone, his successor Massine had gone. As yet, no one had risen to take their place. True, there were good male dancers in the company. Idzikowsky, Woizikowsky, Svereff, were all first-class performers, but in Diaghileff's eyes they lacked the rare, outstanding quality of genius that he looked for. Moreover, these men were fully mature artists, there was nothing further to be got from them. He wanted young talent, that he could influence and inspire as he had done with Nijinsky and Massine. Under his guidance they had reached the full flowering of their individual genius.

The photograph of Anton Dolin still lay on the table before him. Was this the young dancer of the future that he so badly needed? Had this young man the stuff in him of which great artists are made? He had promised well. It might be worth seeing him, but not now, the holidays were here, and for Big Serge the month of August meant Italy and his beloved Venice. Time enough to see this young dancer later when he returned to Paris in September.

Diaghileff picked up a pen and answered Astafieva's letter.

It arrived in London just after Pat's nineteenth birthday.

"September!" Pat was disappointed. "That's nearly two months to wait. Even then he hasn't fixed a date."

"He will write again," Astafieva consoled him. "Of course he will see you. Do you think a man like Diaghileff troubles to write that he will see you when he does not mean it? Stupid boy. Now, we must prepare what you will dance for him."

While Diaghileff and his friends passed the golden hours of August in the sunshine of the Venice Lido, Pat worked on in the airless heat of a London Studio.

September came and the anxiously awaited letter arrived.

"I told you Big Serge would not forget Patté," Madame's clear voice called out to him. "You are to go to Paris."

"Did you say Paris?" Pat hurried in, hardly able to believe what he had heard.

"Yes. You will audition at the Théâtre Gaieté Lyrique in two weeks." They looked at each other. The great moment had come at last. An audition with Diaghileff was a golden opportunity. Was Pat now strong enough to grasp it?

27

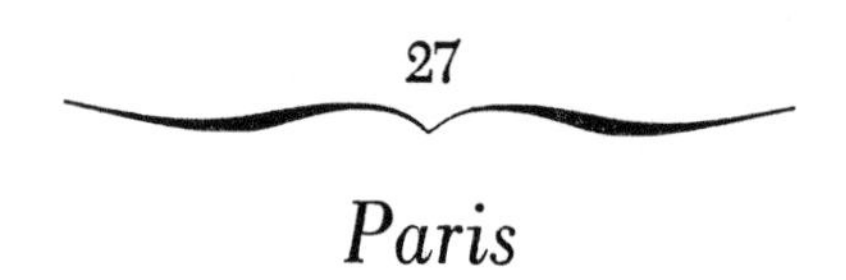

Paris

THREE EXCITED people prepared to travel to Paris. Pat was accompanied by a young fellow-pupil, Jois Berry, who was to be his partner for the audition, and Madame herself who was to escort them both.

Ever since the arrival of Diaghileff's letter all three had been caught up in the whirl of preparations. There was the final polish to be put on the dances; the trip to be arranged; tickets and passports obtained; music to be sorted out; clothes packed. Finally the great day itself arrived.

The first journey to France.

For Pat a taxi to Victoria where the long boat train waited. How important he felt as he made his way through the flood of people arriving from mere suburban trains, to reach the platform labeled "Continental Departures."

There at the gate was Astafieva looking quite strange in a hat, and Jois Berry, very young and pretty in a new outfit, standing with her mother.

As they went down the platform to find their reserved seats on the train they heard their names called. There was the sound of running steps. The next minute they were surrounded by familiar faces, friends and fellow pupils who had come to see them off and wish them good luck.

The guard's whistle blew and the long train pulled slowly away from the platform, away from the group of smiling faces and waving arms, away from the grimy station. It gathered speed and went racketing past the packed, squalid houses of south London and the thinning suburbs, till it shook itself free of the city and roared out into the open, green country.

They reached Dover where the air blew salt, the sun sparkled on the water and the white-painted channel steamer waited by the long customs sheds.

Soon they were leaning on the rail watching the coast of England recede behind the creaming wake of the propellers. The white cliffs dwindled to a blue-gray outline that slowly disappeared into a misty horizon. The worrying thought that one would be seasick and perhaps too upset to dance was lulled by the calm sea and the sunlight on the water, another good omen.

At Calais an invasion of shouting porters in baggy blue tunics and an unfamiliar torrent of French, pursued the passengers and their luggage through the customs shed and up into the high, waiting train, which was to race them through the flat farmlands of northern France towards the capital.

Not much longer now. As the daylight faded and the train roared through the darkening countryside, scattered lights twinkled out of the gathering dusk, the houses crowded in through the carriage windows and soon they were sliding under the high-domed roof of the Gare du Nord. They had arrived.

Paris, to new travelers emerging timidly from the Gare du Nord, presented a bewildering, rackety spectacle of noise and lights.

Through the lively, rowdy streets a perilous taxi screeched and blared its way to the Rue de Rivoli, to unload three weary but excited travelers at the door of the Savoy Hotel.

They were shown their rooms.

"I will go and let Diaghileff know we have arrived," Madame told Jois and Pat. "He is staying in this hotel himself."

They went to wash and change. Astafieva returned to tell them that the audition was to be at twelve o'clock the next day.

"Since we're free this evening do let's go out and see the sights," Jois pleaded after dinner.

They were all of them as thrilled as children on that first evening in Paris, but Astafieva had to be strict.

"No, it is too late," she told them. "You go to bed early and get a good night's sleep so you dance well tomorrow."

Sleep! How could one sleep in this exciting city whose pulsing night life seemed to beat its way into one's room?

Sleep was a long way from Pat as he stood at the open window looking out into Paris. He leaned on the bar, surveying the long, lighted street below, listening to the mingled sounds of traffic, music and voices; smelling the warm, heady night air of this glamorous city.

The impressions crowded in, but in the center of the confused thoughts that whirled around in his tired brain, the words "twelve o'clock" shone like a white, blinding light. Twelve o'clock would decide his future.

He went to bed at last, to a night of restless tossing and turning, falling into an uneasy sleep at dawn.

Twelve o'clock. The hours passed somehow and Pat was sitting with Jois in the hall of the hotel, his stomach turning over as he watched the hands of the clock creep around. Beside him was the little suitcase containing tights, ballet shoes, clean shirt and socks.

"Ah! There you are." Astafieva came hurrying in. "The car is here."

Outside the hotel entrance a large, black limousine was waiting. Pat's heart seemed to flutter like a trapped bird as he saw in the back seat the broad shoulders and massive head of Serge Diaghileff. Astafieva got in next to him. Pat and Jois sat on little seats facing them. The sleek secretary Boris was in front beside the chauffeur.

Of what was said in that swift journey Pat remembered not a word. Of the streets and buildings they passed he saw nothing. He was seeing only the big man in front of him. Diaghileff was talking and Pat was held by the compelling power of those wide-set eyes that watched him so steadily. He was aware of their strange light, which made him feel they were looking right through him, laying bare all the secret places of his heart. Diaghileff smiled at him suddenly and turned away to talk to Astafieva. As he spoke he gestured with his hands, those sensitive surprisingly small hands that held a dancer's future in their grasp. How vividly Pat remembered the lazy, caressing quality of his voice and the whole power of this man to charm those around him and bend them to his purpose.

The Théâtre Gaieté Lyrique was cold. They climbed endless flights of stairs to the rehearsal room, a bare, draughty place at the top of the building that served by day as a studio, by night as the balcony bar.

In the middle of it a bunch of dancers were rehearsing. Pat's teeth were chattering with cold and emotion as he changed. He came to warm up at the bar, and the familiar exercises gave him back his courage and confidence.

The rehearsal finished and the dancers drifted away. A row of chairs was placed across the room. Pat, looking over his shoulder as he worked, saw Diaghileff invite Astafieva to sit beside him. How serious she looked; she must be nervous too. A tall man hovered in the background. He recognized the stage manager Grigorieff. There was another woman with them; no mistaking those heavy features and pale, untidy hair. Nijinska was also to see him dance.

The pianist had sorted out the music and sat ready. This was it. Pat flexed his legs and feet. Jois gave him a wan smile. They took up their positions. There was a moment of horrible, empty silence. Diaghileff nodded his head. The music of the *Sleeping Princess* filled the studio.

Pat and Jois danced a pas de deux. It was the famous

last act adagio of the *Sleeping Princess* that had been performed by every leading artist since Petipa had created it thirty years before.

After this Jois's part in the audition was over, and Pat was alone. Before the silent scrutiny of those expert eyes he did a Russian dance that Astafieva had chosen and arranged for him.

He was well warmed up to his work now and ready for the third and final dance, his own creation.

The familiar and inspiring music of the *Hymn to the Sun* lifted him out of his surroundings. As he danced he was no longer playing the role of a pagan praying to the sun; he was himself, a young dancer stretching out his arms to the great power who ruled the destiny of the Ballet Russe imploring it to open its doors, to him, a foreigner. It was a passionate prayer into which he poured every feeling that was in him.

There was silence as he finished. The echoes of the piano died away. He saw Diaghileff turn to Astafieva and say something.

He went over to Jois, and they stood together in the corner whispering and watching.

Diaghileff rose to go. The audition was over.

What had the great man thought of it?

Pat was to be kept in suspense for another twenty-four hours.

"I cannot tell you," was all that Astafieva would say.

It was not until the next morning that she came to find him.

"Diaghileff will see you in his apartment now." Even then, he could not guess from her voice what this meant. She would tell him no more.

Diaghileff's room was, as usual, overheated and overcrowded. There were Boris and Grigorieff on a sofa; one or two strange men lurked in the background, and the atmosphere was heavy with cigarette smoke and the scent of almond oil. The windows were shut as always, for Diaghileff lived in terror of draughts.

The big man was sitting at a table smiling as he looked at Pat.

"I want you to join my ballet," he said. His words sent the room spinning around in a mad whirl. Dimly Pat heard the soft, deep voice saying in English to Astafieva, "I want him to join as soon as possible. He must go to Monte Carlo without delay to study with Nijinska. Do you hear that, young man?"

Pat shook himself back to reality.

"Nijinska will prepare you for the roles you are to dance." The lazy voice went on to spread the glittering carpet of his future before him. No corps de ballet work for Anton Dolin. He was joining as a dancer in his own right, to dance his own roles. He was to take part in the next Monte Carlo season in December, and prepare from there to take over leading roles.

"It is most important that you should begin work with Nijinska as soon as possible." He turned to his secretary, "Boris, when does our tour finish?"

"The end of October."

"That will give us not quite a month." Diaghileff looked thoughtful. "It is not long but it will have to do. Yes." He looked full at Pat. "You will join us in Monte Carlo at the beginning of November. You will have to work very hard."

"I will," said Pat, and he meant it with all his heart. The

passionate prayer he had poured into his dance had been answered.

The next day they left Paris to return to London. Pat carried a contract in his pocket. To him it was the most precious document in the world. He, an Englishman, was to be a member of Diaghileff's famous Company. He, an Englishman, was to dance leading roles in the great Ballet Russe.

28

Monte Carlo

November, 1923. A train roared through the night hauling its freight of human lives across the sleeping land of France. Southward they sped through the hours of darkness. As dawn was breaking the long line of coaches slowed and jolted to a halt. Heavy-eyed passengers, grimy and unshaven, rubbed the steam from the windows to read the name Marseilles in staring white letters on the station boards. They had reached the south coast. The long night was over and the gray autumn skies of northern France lay far behind them. This was like waking into another world.

As the train left Marseilles and wound its way along the coast, the sun rose up brilliant and warm in a blue sky. From the carriage windows they looked out on to tumbled red rocks and golden sand thrust out into the sparkling waters of the Mediterranean.

It was after midday when they halted at a tiny wayside station perched on a ledge of rock with a precipitous drop to the sea sparkling below. Monte Carlo. They had arrived.

Pat and his luggage stood on the little platform. The train steamed away and was lost to sight around a bend. A small boy rushed into view.

"*Ascenseur*," he screamed.

Pat was still puzzling it out when a leisurely, baggy-bloused porter took charge of the situation. As Pat followed his luggage into the station yard to be put into a cab, he suddenly saw the explanation. Set against the rock face was a large iron elevator cage. He looked up and got a glimpse of a white balustrade and palm trees overhead, and above them the soaring pile of a massive, ornate building whose gleaming white pinnacles reared up against the blue sky.

"Casino et Théâtre de l'Opera." The porter jerked a horny thumb in its direction.

The Opera House! So this was to be the scene of his work—this great white building that overlooked the sea.

The cab took him through climbing, twisting streets to his hotel. It was a quiet, pleasant place, too quiet he found as he stood alone in his room, for the grinding rattle of the train still sounded in his head. The silence of the room was oppressive. The flame of excitement that burned in him demanded noise, bustle, and restless activity. He paced up and down. For days and weeks past every thought and every plan had been centered on this day. The audition in Paris, the contract, the preparations, the last party at home, the great send-off by his friends, the thrill of the journey, and it had all led up to—what? To this quiet hotel bedroom? What an anticlimax.

A sense of loneliness took hold of Pat. He felt suddenly

shut off and imprisoned in this room. He went out quickly. At least he would move about and have a look at this place that was to be his home. What day of the week was it? Friday. He wondered what the others in the company were doing at this moment, and where they all lived. Perhaps there were some in his hotel. If only he had someone to talk to. Then he remembered with a jolt that he didn't know enough Russian to talk to anyone for long, and he didn't speak a word of French. The sense of loneliness deepened. He wandered disconsolately around the town and went to bed early that night a discouraged, disappointed young man.

The next day, Saturday, stretched bleak and empty before him. Not until Sunday were Diaghileff and his friends due to return. He spent two of the loneliest days he had ever known. He had his solitary meals at the hotel and longed for the haphazard companionship of the studio in London.

On Sunday afternoon arrived a message for Mr. Dolin. He was to dine with Diaghileff that evening!

The loneliness was over.

Dining with Diaghileff meant sitting down to table with six or eight other people as well, a bewildering cosmopolitan crowd of celebrities. Pat, floundering in a conversation of mixed French and Russian, strained to pick up a word here and there, and wondered who they all were.

Big Serge was in great spirits. A successful year lay behind him. His ballets had done well and made money. Now, with pockets full he could plan boldly for the future. He called Pat over to sit beside him and spoke to him of the work he was to do, of the future plans for the Ballet Russe, clever far-seeing plans that opened a glittering prospect before the young dancer. They were to start with a three-month winter season of classical ballets, here in the Opera House. It was to be a safe, money-making season, and a trial run for the new dancer. After that, a tour, and then, if Anton Dolin justified the faith placed in him, he would be launched in Paris, making his big debut as a leading dancer of the Ballet Russe.

The hotel bedroom was no longer lonely when Pat returned to it. His mind reeled with the things he had heard. He realized what a great treasure of golden opportunity Diaghileff was holding out to him. There was more than just personal success too. He felt that on him had fallen the responsibility to show the world that an English dancer could uphold the tradition of the Russian ballet.

Pat looked at himself in the mirror.

"I will prove to the world that an Englishman can dance as well as a Russian," he vowed.

Meanwhile tomorrow still lay ahead, and with it the ordeal of taking his place in the company. He would meet them all at the morning class, with Nijinska. Diaghileff had made him understand that he must be very tactful with Nijinska for she was not altogether pleased to have a foreigner coming into the company.

"You must give her time to get used to you," Diaghileff had said. "To begin with you will work under her in the general class with the rest of the company. Later we shall see about private lessons." He had not explained that Nijinska had flatly refused to give private lessons to "the foreigner." Neither did he mention that the company did not exactly welcome strangers in their midst. These things Pat was to find out for himself.

The rehearsal room in the Opera House was underground. It was long and low-ceilinged. The class was at nine. By half-past eight on that first morning Pat was already there warming up at the bar and feeling as shy and anxious as a new boy on his first day in boarding school.

In ones and twos the company arrived. They all stared curiously at this new dancer who had appeared among them. A few recognized him from the *Sleeping Princess* days and smiled. The girls were more friendly than the men.

Sokolova came over to him. Here at least was a fellow-countryman. They talked together until Nijinska arrived.

The class began and Pat forgot the unspoken hostility about him in the effort of work. He was so used to Astafieva that he found it difficult at first to adapt himself to Nijinska's style of teaching. The principle, of course, was the same, but the handling of it strange and new, and the exercises they did were advanced and complicated. The standard set was very high.

"We have a break now," Sokolova told him as they were dismissed. "Rehearsal this afternoon."

"Does Nijinska take all the rehearsals too?" Pat wanted to know.

"Not all of them, Duckie." Sokolova smiled at him with wise understanding. "Don't worry if she doesn't take much notice of you at first; she will get used to you."

Would she? Pat began to wonder as the days settled down into the routine of work and Nijinska still treated him with a marked lack of interest. He felt that she was merely carrying out instructions that Diaghileff had given her, resenting his presence in the company. As he worked, sweated, and strained under Nijinska's indifferent eyes, he mourned for the friendly encouragement of Astafeiva.

Three ballets were to open the season on November 25th.

"You will dance in *Prince Igor* and in *Cleopatra*," Diaghileff had told Pat. "Small corps de ballet roles only to begin with for there is not much time."

As the ballets took shape on the studio floor, Diaghileff and his friends frequently came to watch the rehearsals. On one occasion Pat was beckoned over.

"I want to present you to a cousin of mine," said Diaghileff. "Paul Koriboute."

Pat bowed politely before the elderly, aristocratic-looking man who stood beside Big Serge.

"I thought it was time you two knew each other." There was an amused twinkle in Diaghileff's eyes. "You are both at the same hotel."

It was the beginning of a pleasant and profitable friendship. Mr. Koriboute was a charming, cultured man, and a lonely one. Like many other Russian aristocrats he was a refugee from the Russian revolution. He and Pat were soon sharing a table at the hotel.

"I do wish you would teach me your language," Pat said to him one day.

"Shall we make a bargain?" Mr. Koriboute suggested in his formal, stilted English. "I teach you Russian, you teach me English. At meal times we must promise that neither of us shall speak his own language."

It was a bargain they both kept. Pat was seriously determined to master this difficult language. Curious Anglo-Russian conversations took place, but they had results. Pat at last began to acquire a certain fluency, and with it he began better to understand the people with whom he was working.

Slowly, gradually, the atmosphere of unspoken hostility began to lift. They became accustomed to the foreigner who worked as one of them, and Diaghileff who saw and understood everything that went on in his company judged that this was the moment to approach Nijinska again about private lessons for Pat. It was not easy. Nijinska still obstinately insisted that there was plenty of young talent in the company which could be brought on. There was the young Serge Lifar, for instance, who showed great promise. Why not train him instead of wasting time on "the foreigner"?

Diaghileff, the diplomat, did not remind her that when Lifar had joined them at the beginning of the year, she had been furious that she should be expected to teach an almost untrained young refugee from Communist Russia. The temperamental Nijinska would not be ordered about or bullied, and Diaghileff with infinite charm and tact, patiently persuaded her that Lifar, who had been dancing seriously for less than a year, was not yet ready for big roles, and that Anton Dolin, who had been with Astafieva for six and a half years, was. He flattered her into understanding how important it was that this young English dancer should be trained to express her ideas in the ballets she created. How could he do justice to her choreography unless she taught him herself?

Diaghileff's charm was irresistible. Grudgingly Nijinska agreed to give Pat a daily, private lesson.

"But not in the rehearsal room," she declared. "I don't want the company to know of this; it will make jealousy."

She agreed that Pat's private lesson should take place in the afternoon on the stage of the local motion picture house.

"But not at once," was her parting shot. "I am too busy. Not until after the opening of the season." Diaghileff, smiling, let her have her way.

The November days drew on and the opening date

loomed near. Rich and fashionable society gathered in Monte Carlo for the winter. The hotels filled, the Casino gambling tables were crowded, and on November 25th the Opera House opened its doors and the curtain went up on the first performance of the season's ballets: the white, clasical purity of *Les Sylphides,* the richly beautiful spectacle of *Cleopatra,* and the blood-stirring dances of *Prince Igor.* Three safe, well-tried favorites, for Big Serge was taking no chances—yet.

Pat's part in them was small, but he put all his heart into his work, and on that first evening he knew the exhilaration of dancing in the perfect conditions Diaghileff created for his ballets. Magnificent artists, beautiful decors faultlessly lit, and impeccable music blended into a complete and satisfying work of art.

The fiery dances of *Prince Igor* brought the evening to a dramatic finish, and the dancers lined up to take their bow. Down came the curtain. As it fell, however, the applause was suddenly mingled with laughter. Out in front, cut off from the others, stood an embarrassed young man. Anton Dolin stood acknowledging the applause as though he had provided the whole evening's entertainment.

"A good omen," Diaghileff said to him afterwards. "Yes, a good omen for the future." He drew Pat aside. "Early in the new year you will make your real debut here. I am reviving *Daphnis and Chloe.* You will dance the lead, partnering Sokolova. Nijinska will teach you your role." He added in a low voice, "You will begin your private lessons with her tomorrow."

"Tomorrow!" Pat looked up swiftly as though he would ask how this miracle had come about.

"I persuaded her." Diaghileff smiled, sketching a swift

gesture with his hand. "She will take you tomorrow afternoon. It is better if you do not mention these lessons to anyone yet." He put his hand on Pat's shoulder. "Nijinska can teach you a great deal." He looked at him intently. "It is for you now to win her over to your side."

29

Nijinska

ONE MORNING, early in December, a notice appeared on the board that set tongues wagging.

"Have you seen the latest notice?" People passed the news on to each other. "There's a rehearsal call for *Daphnis and Chloe* this afternoon, and guess who's dancing Daphnis?"

"I don't know. Idzikowsky I suppose or Vilzak?"

"It's Dolin. He's chosen for the lead to partner Sokolova."

Heads came together to talk over this startling development.

"Let them talk," said Diaghileff when he heard. "They will learn soon enough that this is only the beginning."

Meanwhile Pat had to face renewed hostility from jealous rivals who had imagined that they would be chosen for the part.

"They will get over it." Diaghileff haughtily disregarded the jealousies that threaded like turbulent dark currents below the surface. "If they don't like my decisions they can leave."

To make matters worse, the newcomer had been taken up into the circle of Diaghileff's intimate friends. Anton Dolin was a frequent guest at the table of the great. Jealous eyes saw him placed among the rising young celebrities whom Diaghileff had gathered around him.

A new team of talent was forming here in Monte Carlo during this winter. A new chapter in the story of the Ballet Russe was opening. The old, purely Russian regime was dead, for the revolution had severed the life stream that fed the Ballet Russe with dancers, artists, and musicians. Now Diaghileff was looking to the west, to Europe, for the new, young talent he needed.

Very few were left of the original team that had blazed the way to fame. The Russian artist Bakst was dead, and the glorious riot of color he had created for so many ballets had passed into history. In his place came Marie Laurencin with pale clear hues, and the dark eyed Spaniard, Picasso, with his bold modern handling of pure line and color. Stravinsky had gone his own way, and in his place gathered young French composers, Auric and Poulenc, to be joined soon by Darius Milhaud. With them too came the French writer Jean Cocteau, a restless, witty, brilliant young man already famous.

These were the people in whose hands lay the creation of future ballets. It was an intellectual and highly cultured group of people, but the young Englishman was at a disadvantage for the sparkling, witty talk going on around him was a mixture of French and Russian and he could only listen, struggling to understand.

"What's the matter?" Nijinska asked him as he came to his private lesson after one of these lunch parties.

"Language!" Pat pressed his hands to his aching head.

"Ah! You have been with Serge Pavlovitch and his friends?"

"Yes. Nothing but French and Russian, and they talk of politics and art, of books and music, and Diaghileff expects me to follow for he suddenly asks what I think." Pat shook his head despairingly.

"Understanding will come," Nijinska told him. "Already you have learned much Russian. French will follow."

Pat looked at her swiftly, for her voice was unusually warm and friendly.

"I do want to understand," he said. "For there is so much to learn."

"So! You are beginning to find that out."

"What do you mean?" He was puzzled by her tone.

"I mean that you are beginning to realize at last that you have things to learn outside ballet. You find out that to be a great artist you must have knowledge and culture. You English have no culture. Now you are with the great Diaghileff he educates you. He teaches you that it is not enough to live in a world of ballet shoes. To be great yourself you must appreciate greatness in others, and have knowledge of other arts. Like that he trained my brother, Vaslav. He took him to the great cities in Europe; he showed him the finest paintings and sculptures; he made him listen to concerts and operas, and study books; he let him meet all the most interesting people of the day. That is how he trains his chosen, young artists. He did the same for Leonide Massine, he will do the same for you. He trains the mind and the spirit of the dancer, while I," she smiled, "I train the feet!"

They both laughed.

"Come now, enough talk. To work. Let me see you first walk across the stage and stand in the center there."

To walk and to stand had been the first lesson Nijinska had given him. Pat, astonished and indignant, had been informed that he didn't know how to do either of these things.

"You walk like a tired old woman." Nijinska had given him a cruel imitation of a slouching gait. "You learn to walk straight. Not to strut like a turkey cock, but to be tall and proud like a young god, and stand strongly with your head held well."

At first Pat had thought she was doing this out of spite, but he soon realized he was wrong and that these things were vitally important, to give style and finish to a dancer. Strange that no one had thought to teach him so before, he thought, as he crossed the stage with firm, measured tread.

"That is better," Nijinska told him and they passed to more difficult work.

Pat loved his lessons with her for she taught him so much. Undeterred by her sulks, tempers, and indifference he had worked hard and enthusiastically, and Nijinska, on her side, began to admit to herself that this young man was really sincere and serious about his dancing.

"No." She checked him after he had done a high leap across the stage. "That is not good. The jump should be higher, and spread out." Her hands described a long curve.

"I've tried so often," Pat said, in despair. "I suppose my muscles are not powerful enough. I haven't the feet and legs of Nijinsky."

"It is not only the feet and legs that make a jump." Nijinska looked at him out of the corners of her slanting eyes. She was silent as though she were deciding whether to say more.

"Yes." She turned her head and looked full at Pat. "I will tell you how my brother did his great jumps. It was by the control of breathing, here." She tapped her chest. "You prepare to jump, you breathe deeply, your body is full of air, and you stay up. Look I show you. First I breathe as you do, anyhow." Nijinska ran across the stage and demonstrated. "You see, I am heavy, my muscles must do all the work, it seems to be a great effort, that is bad."

Pat thought it was wonderful but said nothing.

"Now. I do it our way. I control my breathing." She seemed to sail up into the air in an effortless movement. What tremendous power she had for a woman.

"Now." Nijinska came back to him. "I teach you to do the same." Pat looked at her with sudden emotion, realizing that she was passing on to him the secret of her brother's famous elevation. He knew then that the last barriers were broken down between them. At last Nijinska was on his side.

The bright, sunny days passed swiftly for Pat in a mounting pressure of work. The routine of each day followed its inexorable rhythm: the morning class, the afternoon rehearsal, the private lesson, the evening performance. Lunches and dinners with Diaghileff and his friends, and all the time a growing knowledge of French and Russian. It was a hard, exacting life, but Pat was utterly happy in it.

The opening of *Daphnis and Chloe* was fixed for January 1st.

On New Year's Eve the dancers were in the theatre getting ready for the last dress rehearsal when startling news broke.

"Idzikowsky is gone!" It passed from mouth to mouth

like a fire, spreading consternation in the dressing-rooms. Doors were opened and little knots of people gathered in the corridors.

There was a further wave of excitement as Nijinska arrived.

"All is well." Pat's dresser brought him the news. "Madame Nijinska is dancing Idzikowsky's role herself. The situation is saved."

"A man's role?" Pat frowned.

"It will not be noticed in that costume." The dresser chuckled, thinking of Nijinska stepping, literally, into Idzikowsky's discarded trousers.

"That's all right then." Pat, putting the finishing touches to his make-up, was more concerned with his own coming ordeal than the drama going on around him.

Later, on thinking it over, he was to realize that the unceremonious departure of Idzikowsky would mean that many important roles would fall vacant, and that probably he would have the chance to take them on.

There was a knock on the door.

"It is a lady to see you," his dresser told him. "She would not give her name."

"No," he said, "I can't see anyone now. Ask her to come after the rehearsal . . ." He broke off, hearing a noise and turned around. The door of the dressing-room was open. There, standing smiling at him, was Astafieva.

"Madame!" Pat ran to greet her with open arms. Surprise and delight were complete. Out of the torrent of broken English and Russian, he gathered that this was all Diaghileff's idea. He had invited Astafieva to come from London as his guest so that she could see her pupil's debut.

"Dear Big Serge, he thinks of everything."

Dear Madame! Her familiar reassuring presence seemed to fill Pat's dressing-room. How lovely she looked. The wonderful hands, the vivid face. What a lot they had to say to each other.

Pat danced the dress rehearsal that night on winged feet. Time enough for nerves at the opening tomorrow. They danced to a privileged group of people in the orchestra whom Diaghileff had invited. After it was over Sokolova and Pat were summoned around to the front. Here they were presented to a distinguished looking gentleman. There was a twinkle in Diaghileff's eyes as Sokolova curtseyed and Anton Dolin bowed low before his Royal Highness, the Duke of Connaught, who discovered, to his surprise, that the two leading dancers of the Russian Ballet were fellow countrymen.

He was friendly and charming and they withdrew from his presence with royal wishes for a Happy New Year.

In the stress of the dress rehearsal they had almost forgotten that tomorrow would be 1924. For Pat, though he could not know it yet, those good wishes were to be royally fulfilled. 1924 was, indeed, to be a very happy year.

30

The New Year

ON THE FIRST DAY of the New Year, the second ballet of the evening introduced, for the first time, a young English dancer in a leading role.

It was twelve years since the curtain had gone up on *Daphnis and Chloe*. Those years, however, had not dimmed the glorious colors of Bakst's scenery, and the audience of 1924 saw the same green and leafy grove sacred to the god Pan, and luminous with sunshine and blue sky. They heard the music that Ravel had written weaving the same enchantment into this pagan setting of old Greek mythology. In place of the legendary figures of Karsavina and Nijinsky though, there now stood the English dancers of the new generation, Sokolova and Anton Dolin.

Anton Dolin and Nijinsky. Did Diaghileff realize the ordeal he had set his young Dolin by bringing him for the first time before an expert and critical public to dance, almost literally, in Nijinsky's shoes? Since the great Russian had created the role of Daphnis, no one else had danced it. Tonight, therefore, the young Englishman would be measured against the standard set by a man who was acknowledged to be the greatest dancer of his day, and, some people considered, of all time. There never would be another Nijinsky, they said—or would there?

The overture was finishing and in the wings stood Anton Dolin, a graceful, boyish figure in Daphnis' short white tunic. He waited for his entrance, a prey to first-night nerves, trying not to let himself think of failure, or of the critics who were waiting out there, he imagined, to tear him to pieces. It was only the thought of his friends, the people who had helped him and believed in him, that gave him the courage to go out on to that stage—to be judged.

The judgment was summed up by one of the critics afterwards. The great André Levinson wrote:

"Anton Dolin, that strong and beautiful young man, has made a promising beginning, though rather a premature one.

His professional skill is rudimentary. He does however execute high leaps quite well. If his miming lacks subtlety, it is, nevertheless, not clumsy. Without being expressive, his acting is anything but stilted, and his youth, well in evidence, is on his side."

"What an unkind write-up," was Pat's first indignant reaction. He read it again and took comfort in realizing that it might have been much worse. He had made a "promising beginning." Enough that he had come through the first trial and survived. "A promising beginning"—Pat took heart again. He was further encouraged when he learned that Diaghileff was pleased, Nijinska was pleased, Astafieva was proud and delighted, and in the eyes of the company he had done well. Anton Dolin, they considered, had deserved the laurel wreaths he had won. They accepted him as one of them and warmed to friendliness.

Pat felt that he had passed another milestone on his hard, upward journey. It was indeed a happy beginning to the New Year.

After this things were to go more easily. He was now living and working in an atmosphere of friendliness and encouragement. *Daphnis and Chloe* passed into the regular repertoire, and already Diaghileff was planning three new ballets to follow.

"I want you to dance in two of them," he told Pat. "Small parts only. That will be enough while you still study with Nijinska."

Pat understood clearly now that his training and career were in master hands. He was being steadily and skilfully prepared for great things. Success in Paris was the ultimate goal. Diaghileff was a dictator where his company was concerned. He had made it clear to Pat from the beginning that he was the master, that he made his dancers and ruled their destinies. Not until later would Pat's proud and independent spirit rebel. For the present he was grateful for all the things Diaghileff was doing for him, and content that it should be so.

Diaghileff had told him that he would make his debut in Paris in *Daphnis and Chloe* sometime in the summer. Meanwhile, the Monte Carlo winter season was in full swing. New rehearsals started in the long, underground room.

The first of the new ballets, *Les Tentations de la Bergère,* was a fragile, Dresden shepherdess creation. Pat found he was partnering Tchernicheva.

"You are a god and goddess." Nijinska set them to work to learn their pas de deux.

They were hard at work on it when the door from the office opened. A thin, lively face appeared.

"Ah! I see you are busy with La Bergère." Jean Cocteau came tripping gaily into the room. "Have you seen the costumes these two are to wear?"

"No," said Nijinska, concentrating on her dancers.

"I saw the designs this morning." Jean Cocteau perambulated around the piano. "Would you believe it, the god and goddess are to be dressed exactly alike." He came across the studio imitating the steps they had just been doing.

"Jean, go away. I want to get on with my rehearsal." Nijinska was trying not to laugh at his antics.

"In pink rosebuds!" Jean cocked a mischievous eye in her direction. "We shan't know which is Tchernicheva and which is Dolin! Think of the possibilities that creates," and the *enfant terrible* of the place darted around in a circle, making them all laugh.

"What is going on in here?" The broad figure of Diaghileff filled the open doorway. "Jean, it is you, up to your nonsense again!" He came into the studio followed by an artist who carried a portfolio under his arm.

"We were thinking of letting Tchernicheva lift Dolin on to her shoulder; the effect should be decidedly quaint." Jean was quite irrepressible. "Ah! Here are the designs." He went darting across to the artist Juan Gris. Rehearsals were suspended while Nijinska joined a committee meeting that gathered over the sketches.

The dancers hung about waiting. Pat drifted away to the far end of the studio. For rehearsals the long room was divided across the middle by a curtain. Pat pushed his way through it to find three or four of the men leaning against the bar talking. He joined them, and found to his surprise that they were discussing acrobatics.

"Of course it will never take the place of ballet," one of them was saying. "This craze for modern acrobatic dancing is only a passing fashion."

"They are very clever, some of these people," another put in. "I saw a remarkable couple at the Casino at Nice last week. They had amazing balance and control."

"Those things are only tricks," said one scornfully. "Any well-trained classical dancer could do them with a little practice."

"Try them yourself then," he was challenged.

"I used to do some of their tricks to amuse myself." Pat joined in the conversation. "They're not really difficult if you have a good sense of balance and don't mind falling over."

A few minutes later, if Diaghileff or Nijinska had looked around the curtain, they would have been greeted by the edifying sight of their classical dancers tumbling over the floor in a series of wild acrobatics.

"It is really much more difficult than it looks," they admitted, and it was not long before they had all given up to stand and admire Pat.

"How did you learn to do it?" they wanted to know as he stood on his hands and slowly shifted his balance till he was supported on one hand alone.

"I don't really know." Pat came the right way up again. "I used to practice for fun when I was a boy, and I found it came quite easily. There is one thing I'd like to try that I've never had the chance to do before and that is to be swung around."

"Oh yes, the couple at Nice did that."

"Come on, let's try it."

None of them saw the curtain move, and a bright, inquiring face appear. Jean Cocteau, bored with the costume discussion, had come in search of other interest. He found it. He saw the body of Diaghileff's new leading dancer whirling around in the air, an arm and a leg held in the grip of a muscular member of the corps de ballet.

The rest of Jean Cocteau came around the curtain to see better.

He leaned against the bar watching intently as Pat followed it up with different tricks. For once Jean forgot to be witty or clever. He was quite silent, absorbed in the movements of that supple athletic body. Pat was realizing just how much he had missed his "hobby," and was thoroughly enjoying himself. For long months, these acrobatics of his had been forgotten in the stress of strict ballet training.

"What you do there is very interesting," said Jean as he finished.

"I'm out of practice," Pat told him.

"Then you must get in practice again," Jean replied seriously.

"As long as Nijinska doesn't see me!" Pat laughed.

He did practice again. Whenever there were spare moments at rehearsals he would disappear behind the curtain to the deserted half of the studio and amuse himself trying out different tricks. Whatever he did, though, he tried to carry out with the style and grace of a dancer. He wedded his acrobatics to his classical dancing.

Sometimes he was alone; more often though, the still, silent figure of Jean Cocteau would be there, leaning against the bar, and as he watched the lively, brilliant brain was active, for the sight of a classical dancer doing acrobatics had struck a spark and given Jean Cocteau a powerful new idea—an idea that was to grow into *The Blue Train.*

31

New Plans

IN FEBRUARY the ballet season finished. Diaghileff and his friends prepared to migrate to Paris. Only the corps de ballet were to remain in Monte Carlo to take part in the Opera season that followed.

"Nijinska will be too busy to give you lessons here," Diaghileff told Pat. "She has to prepare the dances for the Operas. I have arranged for you to go to Paris. You will study with Trefilova."

Pat was delighted. He didn't want to be left behind in the south of France after the others had gone.

So, once again, he stood on Monte Carlo's wayside station, waiting, this time, for the Paris Rapide. Was it only three months since an excited young man had climbed down from the train at this same station and had had his first glimpse of the theatre towering up through the palm trees, dazzling white against the blue sky? How strange and frightening everything had been. Now, the young leading dancer of the Russian Ballet could smile at that other timid figure. He was no longer the stranger and the new boy. He had made his successful debut in Monte Carlo. Before him now lay the final test of Paris. It was a challenge that made his heart beat strongly.

The dusty green train came whistling and screeching around the bend. Pat climbed up into it. In a few hours they had left the sunlit Mediterranean and the palm trees and were headed north on the long journey across France.

In Paris Pat found a message waiting for him at his hotel.

"Come to lunch tomorrow. D."

Boris Kochno met him in the foyer of the hotel.

"Serge Pavlovitch is full of plans for a new ballet." He linked his arm through Pat's and the two young men made their way into the dining-room. "It's been specially written for you."

Questions came piling into Pat's mind, but there was no time to ask them, for he was face to face with big Serge. Those strange, light eyes were looking deeply into him, as though Diaghileff wanted to assure himself there was no change. Swiftly it was over and Pat was enfolded in a warm Russian greeting.

He shook hands with Igor Stravinsky.

"Now, I want you to meet another musician." Diaghileff still had his arm about Pat's shoulders as he presented him to a dark-haired man of massive build. It was Darius Milhaud, the French composer.

The others at table were old friends. Pablo Picasso was there with his beautiful Russian wife, Olga, who had herself been a dancer in the Ballet Russe. Jean Cocteau too, mischievous and irrepressible as ever.

"Has le Grand told you?" he greeted Pat as they all sat down to lunch. "I have written a ballet for you. A new ballet in a new style. It will be the most modern thing ever seen."

Diaghileff leaned across to Pat.

"We want a ballet for your debut in Paris."

"So, I have created *Le Train Bleu* especially for the occasion!" Jean was bubbling with enthusiasm for his idea. "And Darius Milhaud here is to write the music."

"But I thought I was to dance in *Daphnis and Chloe?*"

"That is what I intended but we ran into trouble over the performing rights." Diaghileff turned to Boris. "What was it exactly?"

"It appears that we cannot put on a performance of *Daphnis and Chloe* in Paris," the smooth Boris explained. "It seems that the Paris Opera Ballet Company own the performing rights."

"So," Diaghileff gestured, "we must find another ballet to present you to the Paris public, and Jean, here, arrived with his idea for something entirely new."

"When is this to be?" Pat asked.

"In the early summer. I am arranging a season here for May," Diaghileff told him. "We go on tour to Spain first. We shall have about three months to prepare the Paris season, so we must get this new ballet *The Blue Train* into rehearsal as soon as we can."

"What! With the music not even written," remarked Stravinsky dryly.

"I have already one or two themes I have been working on," put in Darius Milhaud.

The Blue Train was the center around which their talk revolved, while hovering waiters brought the caviar, the sole meunière, the entrecôtes, and the wines flowed. Pat listened and learned about this ballet that was being specially created for him.

"When I saw you doing your acrobatics down in the studio," Jean explained to him, "the idea came to me of acrobatics on the beach. I pictured the smart young people who go to the fashionable seaside places . . ."

"I think I shall get Chanel to design the costumes," Diaghileff interrupted.

"But she is not a stage designer," remarked Picasso.

"No, but she is the smartest woman in Paris, and a leader of fashion. She should be able to dress for the stage as well as *le monde*."

"Undress," put in Jean swiftly. "It will be bathing costumes."

"You two must get together." Diaghileff turned to his secretary. "Boris, remind me to arrange a dinner so that Jean and Coco can fight about what the dancers are not to wear."

"What role am I dancing?" Pat tried to find out. "What is the story of the ballet?"

"There is no story," said Jean Cocteau airily. "That is the point. It is an expression of modern life. These young people are on the beach; by their attitudes and movements they symbolize modern life. They swim, they play tennis, golf, and beach games. Their dances will express all these. You are the swimmer, the Beau Gosse, and the center of attention."

"And my music will be modern, syncopated rhythm," Darius Milhaud joined in. "The music of the present day."

"*The Blue Train* will be the forerunner of the ballets of the future." The force of Diaghileff's enthusiasm infected them all. "We shall show people that the Ballet Russe leads the way. As soon as Nijinska has finished at Monte Carlo, she must get to work on the choreography."

"What will Nijinska say when she learns that she has to do the choreography for modern acrobatics?" inquired Picasso.

"She will get used to it." Diaghileff's hand smoothed over Nijinska's feelings. "She will be dancing in it herself."

"There are four principal roles," Jean put in. "The Beau Gosse and Perlouse, that is you and Sokolva. The tennis champion and the golfer, Nijinska and Woizikowsky."

"It is the first time a ballet has ever been written around an individual dancer," remarked Stravinsky.

"Yes, that is true," said Serge. "You are a very honored young man."

"It is not every day you find a classical dancer who is also a skilled acrobat," put in Jean Cocteau swiftly.

"How many others will take part?" Darius Milaud was asking.

"About a dozen? Twenty? Jean shrugged his shoulders,

looking at Diaghileff. "They are the casual, modern young people one finds on the smart beaches."

"I want Lifar to have a small role in this ballet." Diaghileff was speaking half to himself, staring into the glass of champagne he held in his hand.

"That young man is coming on well," said Jean. "I was noticing him at Monte Carlo. You have a future dancer there, Serge."

"The future of Lifar is for me to decide," said Diaghileff coldly. "Moreover, I will not have people spoiling members of my corps de ballet. You gave Serge Lifar a great deal more attention than was good for him. I want that young man kept in his place to work." Those words made Pat feel much better.

"There is the English girl," Diaghileff went on. "What's her name?"

"Ninette de Valois," suggested Jean.

"Yes. That's the one." Diaghileff made a point of not remembering her name because he disliked it. It annoyed him that she wouldn't Russianize it. "She will do perhaps to dance opposite Lifar."

"Why don't you use that girl for bigger roles?" asked Jean.

"She is not suitable," said Serge. "She is a nice dancer but not yet ready."

"I think you are very hard on her, to keep her in your corps de ballet after she has danced leading roles in London."

"She did not have to join my company," retorted Diaghileff, "and she does not have to stay in it."

"Why don't you give her a chance to show herself?"

"Are you trying to tell me how to run my company?" There was a dangerous light in Diaghileff's eyes.

"Yes," said Jean solemnly. "You know perfectly well I can run it better than you."

Big Serge laughed and they went on to discuss other dancers who would take part.

The lunch party broke up at last, with enthusiasm at fever heat for *The Blue Train*.

"No, young man," Diaghileff checked Pat as he was taking his leave with the others. "You are not to run away. You are coming with me this afternoon to visit the Louvre. While you are in Paris your artistic education shall be attended to."

They walked together through the long galleries of the massive gray palace that houses the collection of some of the world's greatest paintings. Diaghileff was a remarkable guide. Pat was impressed yet again by the profound culture and knowledge of this incredible man.

"Pictures were my first love," he told Pat as they came to stand before the *Mona Lisa*. "In the years before the war I organized exhibitions of Russian art here in Paris. The public flocked to my salons. To them the works of our Russian painters were a revelation. After this, I brought into Europe our Russian dancers, and they were an even greater sensation. Yes, with my ballets I bring the public living pictures." He leaned heavily on his stick and a sad expression came into his eyes as he looked at the smiling face of the *Mona Lisa*.

"I am often envious of these painted canvases," he said slowly, "for their beauty can endure. The pictures an artist creates may hang on a wall for generations to see and love, while the pictures I create, my ballets, are but moments of passing beauty. They can live only in the fading memories of those who have seen them."

He looked away from the painted face on the canvas to the living face of the young dancer beside him, and his voice was deep with the yearning sadness that lies in every Russian heart.

"I would that I, too, could capture forever in some enduring form the youth and beauty that I give to the world."

32

Spain

AN EXPRESS TRAIN rattled and roared through the night with its dimly lit crowded coaches and slumbering passengers. In the early hours of the morning they crossed the frontier, and headed into Spain.

To the remorseless beat of the wheels, Pat's weary brain went over and over the steps he was to dance this very night, steps that he had been rehearsing ceaselessly for days past. It was April now. Nearly a month ago he had been recalled suddenly from Paris to learn the leading roles in *Les Sylphides* and *Pulcinella*. As he had foreseen, Idzikowsky's dramatic departure from the company on the eve of *Daphnis and Chloe* had left a gap in the ranks of the leading male dancers, and Diaghileff had called on Pat to step into Idzikowsky's place. Tonight, in Barcelona, he was to dance these two roles for the first time.

His role in *Pulcinella* was a long and exacting one. *Les Sylphides* he loved. He had the only male part in it, and was partnering Nemchinova. As he thought of this ballet, through the thunder of the wheels he seemed to hear again the swelling sounds of Chopin's lovely music. He could feel himself move across the stage, floating with Nemchinova in his arms, floating...

"Barcelona! Barcelona!" Shouting voices and stamping feet awoke Pat with a start. He had fallen asleep after all. Now the sun was shining. It was eight in the morning; the long night journey was over. They had arrived.

Barcelona, city of sunshine, dust and dirt; strange smells, strange language, and strange rattling taxis that distributed the weary company and their luggage at their various hotels. Bath, breakfast, and sleep before rehearsals. That very same afternoon the dancers gathered on the stage of the Liceo Theatre. Grigorieff was on the look-out for Pat.

"Ah! Dolin!" The tall stage manager came up to him. "I have a telegram." He waved the paper about in a wide sweep. "Nemchinova she is ill." He made poetic gestures in the direction of his neck and ears.

"He means she's got mumps," Sokolova translated.

A ballerina with mumps! How unromantic, but what a crisis for the company.

"You must dance *Les Sylphides* tonight with Sokolova." Grigorieff smiled and spread out his graceful hands. "We must rehearse now. Yes?"

Pat and Sokolova looked at each other. Pat thought of the hours he had practiced this role with Nemchinova. Now, at the last minute, he had to start all over again with a new partner.

"Have you danced it before?" he asked her.

"Never," said Sokolova cheerfully. "I have been eleven years with the company and I have never danced the pas de deux in *Les Sylphides.*"

"Then you will start now and learn it," said Grigorieff calmly.

She did.

They worked almost until the curtain went up at ten o'clock. Somehow they got it ready and Sokolova and Dolin made their debut together in *Les Sylphides.*

Between them they got through the ballet successfully and the rest of the program went without a hitch.

It was one o'clock when the curtain came down.

"Do they always play as late as this?" Pat asked.

"Yes," he was told. "In Spain everything is much later. They seem to sleep in the day and come to life at night."

There was no sleeping in the day for the company, however. For them work started as usual at nine o'clock in the morning. The daily, two-hour lesson was a rigorous part of their discipline from which no one could hope to escape.

On the second day a notice went up on the board at the theatre.

"First Rehearsal of *The Blue Train,* April 25th, 2 o'clock." Underneath was pinned a list of names.

The dancers in practice clothes gathered on the bare stage. There was much talk and guessing about this new ballet that had suddenly come upon them.

Pat stood a little apart from the others, listening and saying nothing. He was remembering the lunch in Paris when he had first heard of this ballet that was written for him. Later he had been invited to dine with Diaghileff to meet Coco Chanel who was to design the costumes, and Laurens, the sculptor, who was to do the decor. By then

Milhaud's music was already written. They had all listened to this ultramodern score of syncopated rhythms and strange disharmonies. After it they had sat late into the night talking, planning, and clothing the idea of *The Blue Train* with color and movement.

He wondered what the company would think when they discovered that the ballet had been especially created for him.

The babble of talk died away to silence. Serge Diaghileff came on to the stage with Boris and Grigorieff.

A chair was brought, and Diaghileff signed to his dancers to gather around him.

He began to talk in Russian. In his deep, attractive voice that knew so well how to play on the minds and feelings of those who heard it, he spoke to them of modern music. He explained that the modern composers like Stravinsky and Strauss deliberately did away with the old-fashioned melody and theme, that in their work they went all out for colorful rhythms, for quick brusque movement and discords that expressed the restless, nervous pulse of modern life. Then he spoke of the music of Darius Milhaud.

"In his music you see the shape of things to come," the persuasive voice went on. "You are already familiar with the rhythm of the machine age, and the poetry of the transatlantic skyscraper. Now you must accept this new poetry, the music of the street. Yes, we must take it very seriously, this new music which comes from the streets. It is the music of tomorrow. My Russian Ballet is the artistic advance guard. We cannot mark time and live the life of yesterday. We cannot even live the life of today. We have to look to tomorrow, and see into the future, for we are the leaders of the world. It is for us to guide the crowd, and reveal to them the things that no one else has seen yet. I attach a great importance to this new ballet, and I want you to do the same."

They stood around him, listening intently to this compelling, forceful man. His words aroused in them a tremendous urge to succeed, to carry this new ballet into the forefront of modern dancing.

Diaghileff went on to tell them of the general theme of the ballet, with details of the different roles in it. With his usual skill in handling people, he whipped up their enthusiasm. They went to work with tremendous drive on the first rehearsal of *The Blue Train.*

33

Preparing the Paris Season

May time in Paris. The broad avenue of the Champs Élysées was alive with movement and sunshine. Restless traffic passed in a glittering colored stream flowing between the wide Place de la Concorde and the distant Arc de Triomphe, standing on the crest of the slope, aloof and beautiful against the skyline.

Under the bright awnings of the cafés the colored tables were filled, for in Paris there is always time to sit at a terrace and watch the smart people strolling to and fro on the wide shady pavements. The sounds of tapping feet and quick French voices, and the hum of traffic, swelling into a great symphony of springtime as the colorful life of Paris beat and throbbed along this great artery.

Halfway along the Champs Élysées, a quieter, tree-shaded avenue cuts a straight broad line through the tall gray houses to the river. Here on the spring days of 1924 there were cars parked in the shade of the trees outside the entrance of a tall new building. People came and went through the wide doorways, above which the letters, cut into the white stone, spelled out "Théâtre des Champs Élysées." Already the posters were up on the boards outside, splashing the news that the Ballet Russe de Monte Carlo, under the direction of Serge Diaghileff, would shortly open their eighth Paris season. Two new ballets were listed for the opening: *Les Fâcheux* and *Les Biches.* No mention yet of *The Blue Train,* but the new name, Anton Dolin, was displayed prominently, in bold black type.

"Who is this new dancer?" people were asking. What surprises had Diaghileff in store for them now? Curiosity and interest were aroused.

"Tell me, Mr. Dolin, is it true that you are an Englishman?" A newspaper reporter was sitting in the makeshift office at the back of the stage interviewing this rising new star of the Ballet Russe, that was so soon to shine in Paris.

"Yes, I am English," Pat looked across at Diaghileff as though to say, "Please, release me from this," but the big man only leaned back in his chair, fanned himself with a program, and smilingly told the reporter that it was the first time in the history of the Russian Ballet that leading roles were to be entrusted to an Englishman.

"And a very young one too," the reporter tactfully suggested.

"I am nineteen," said Pat, and watched the man write it down.

"Phenomenal young Englishman of nineteen makes his debut with the Russian Ballet." The reporter was already seeing his article take shape.

Pat went on to answer endless personal questions about his home, his training, his life in England.

"Is it true that you are making your first appearance in Paris in a ballet that has been specially written for you?"

"Well, not exactly." Pat hesitated and looked to Diaghileff.

"It is correct that *The Blue Train* has been written for him." Big Serge screwed in his monocle and fixed the reporter with it. "But it will not be given until the second week. During the opening week of the season Anton Dolin will appear in *Les Fâcheux*."

Boris Kochno looked in.

"The photographer from *Paris Match* is here," he announced.

The reporter was rapidly disposed of and Pat was taken away to be put under glaring lights, posed and photographed from all angles.

When it was over Boris brought him back to the office where Diaghileff was deep in talk with Jean Cocteau.

"You have a costume fitting at four o'clock." Boris picked up the list of his appointments. "After that, an interview with *Samedi Soir;* they are probably sending a photographer too."

Pat made a face. More interviews, more silly questions. It had been amusing at first, but by now he was already bored with it.

Nijinska came in.

"Can I have Dolin for rehearsal now?" she inquired.

"I hope so." Pat longed to get away.

"Tomorrow," Diaghileff said to them, "I have invited some important people to watch *The Blue Train* rehearsals in the afternoon."

"Oh!" said Nijinska blankly, "that means we get no work done."

Pat silently agreed with her. Important people to rehearsal meant clean shirts, new shoes, being on one's best behavior and giving a performance rather than having a rehearsal.

"What are you rehearsing with Dolin now?" Serge asked Nijinska.

"*Les Fâcheux,*" she replied. "Our room is free. I have sent the rest of the company to lunch."

"Interviews, photographs, fittings, public rehearsals," Pat grumbled as he made his way to the room where he practiced privately with Nijinska. "It never stops."

"That is the price you must pay for success," she told him. "The lights are on you all the time, and your life becomes public property."

"Yes, even rehearsals," Pat went on. "At least no one can see these." He prepared for his work.

Les Fâcheux was a ballet that Boris Kochno had adapted from Molière. It had first been performed in January at Monte Carlo, following *Les Tentations de la Bergère.* Now it was to open the Paris season.

Diaghileff had hoped to include *The Blue Train* in the opening night, but as it was not going to be ready in time, he had had a special part written into *Les Fâcheux* for Pat. He was to play the role of L'Élégant, appearing towards the end of the ballet in a short solo dance as the elegant, affected Dandy.

In this private room he and Nijinska were preparing a surprise for the rest of the company as well as for the public. Once again, Pat was making history.

For the first time, a male dancer would appear on the stage dancing on his points.

"You will make the danseuses jealous," chuckled Nijinska as Pat turned four neat pirouettes on his toes with the grace and accomplishment of a ballerina. "They will never believe that it comes to you naturally."

Her words sent Pat's thought back over the years to the little girl in the blond wig who had made her first appearance on the stage of the Brighton Hippodrome on her toes. What a curious turn of the wheel of fate that he was to make his first appearance in Paris on his toes. It would be amusing, original, but that was all. For Pat, the affected, lace-ruffled Dandy in a long skirted coat and embroidered knee breeches, who appeared in *Les Fâcheux*, was but a prelude. The important work, the one thing that mattered and on which all his hopes and thoughts were focused was his own ballet, *The Blue Train.*

Everything that had gone before—his success in Monte Carlo and Barcelona—faded and dwindled into insignificance. He felt now that all these had been but a rehearsal, a preparation, for the big event.

The days went by and the opening night of the season was on them. The curtain went up on *Les Fâcheux,* and Anton Dolin made his debut in Paris, on his toes.

The ballet itself did not arouse great enthusiasm among the critics. For them, only one thing stood out in it, and that was the performance of Anton Dolin.

One of them wrote afterwards:

"Only Dolin saved the ballet from complete insignificance by a brilliant effort in its final section."

The critics had called his first trial in Monte Carlo, "a promising beginning." Now they called his prelude, "a brilliant effort." What were they going to say about the real thing?

34

Last Rehearsals

"REHEARSAL OF *The Blue Train* 2:30." The daily notices went up. Only a week left now before its premiere. Everyone's thoughts and attention were centered on this new production. Time was running short and there was still much to be done.

By half-past two on a sunny afternoon in June the temperature inside the theatre had risen uncomfortably. On the drab, bare stage, thirty dancers worked and sweated in the heat. The iron safety curtain was down, shutting them off from the dark and empty auditorium, and against it stood a table and chairs. On one side was the piano, the young Russian accompanist frowning over the unfamiliar manuscript score of Milhaud's music. In a corner Picasso stood talking to Grigorieff, and near them were Madame Picasso and her little son who watched the dancers, entranced. Jean Cocteau, nervy and anxious, hovered about ever on the alert, ready to jump in and find fault. In the center, Nijinska, in a black practice dress, pale-faced and tired, her hair scratched up in an untidy bun, directed operations.

"No, Dolin, that is not what I want." A vivid gesture swept aside his movement. "It is not like that. See, I show you." Her tired face lit up and her whole body seemed transformed with new life as she danced the movement he was to copy.

"And then you do your jumps in this direction." She went around the stage in a series of high and beautiful leaps, and, suddenly, through the silence, came a shrill childish voice.

"Look, Papa! Is she never going to come down again?" There was Picasso's small son tugging at his father's hand and staring open-mouthed at this magnificent sight.

Nijinska heard him and laughed, and they all forgot for a moment that they were hot, sweating and tired. Picasso Junior had a great deal more to say, but his running commentary was drowned in the noise of the piano and the beat of feet.

"Now, Dolin, this is where you come over," Nijinska called out, and Pat whirled across the stage in a series of cartwheels.

The music changed.

"Now the backfalls . . ."

As Pat stood ready to begin, he became aware of a curious silence around him. The atmosphere had grown suddenly strange. Everyone seemed to be looking in the same direction. Pat turned too, and saw that the large scenic door at the back had opened. Through it was coming a man, moving slowly towards them. It was a strange figure that glided rather than walked as though he were not sure of his feet.

A name was whispered from one to the other and a deep hush fell over the whole company; a tense, painful silence, centered on that gliding figure.

They were watching Vaslav Nijinsky move on to the stage. Behind him, with Serge Diaghileff, followed his wife, Romola Nijinska, and valet.

Slowly he walked down to the safety curtain and sat down.

In awe and pity the young Anton Dolin stared at this living tragedy of the great dancer on whom he had built all his ideals, the man whose achievements had inspired him and spurred him on. The face and body of Nijinsky still resembled the faded photograph that stood in Astafieva's room in London: the same shaped eyes, the same beautiful mouth, but there was a terrible blankness in the look, and his helpless hands moved and fidgeted continually.

Big Serge leaned over and said something. They saw Nijinsky smile and shake his head but he didn't speak. Did he understand what that voice he knew so well was saying to him? He gave no sign. There was an infinite depth of sadness and tenderness in Big Serge's eyes as he looked at the pathetic, broken figure of this artist he had created. The magnificent body was there; if only the broken threads of the mind that controlled it could be mended. Diaghileff, hoping against hope, had poured out his own money to send Nijinsky to the greatest brain specialists in Europe, but none had been able to cure him. So he lived on, day after day, in his flat in Paris, tended by his devoted wife and valet, and seeing, without understanding, his daughter growing up into a lovely child. Would she too be a dancer? Had she inherited her father's genius? The years to come would show; meanwhile, Nijinsky sat staring in front of him and his restless hands were never still.

Unbearably moved, Pat looked away, and he saw the tragedy of that broken life reflected in the eyes of all those who looked on it. Sokolova's face was white, Bronislava Nijinska's eyes were wet with tears.

"I can't go on." She leaned on Pat's shoulder. "I can't go on; it's too awful."

Pat, finding no words, put his arm about her to give her courage, and felt her body shaking with emotion, while her brother sat on the chair, as helpless as an invalid, staring at the dancers before him with eyes that saw but could convey nothing to that poor, dazed brain.

Somehow they got the rehearsal going again, and this god of the dance, he who did not jump but flew like a bird, sat and watched his successor Anton Dolin doing backfalls, cartwheels, and classical acrobatics.

What did he think of it all, Pat wondered. What were his feelings as he watched, but no one would ever know, for Nijinsky did not speak, and presently he rose. His wife took his arm and, as quietly as he had come, he went out of the gloom of the theatre into the sunshine of Paris.

The work continued. *The Blue Train* struggled on into existence. It was a hard struggle, but out of the clash of temperament and conflicting ideas the new ballet was slowly forged.

Jean Cocteau and Nijinska quarreled incessantly over the scenario and choreography. Hours were wasted in discussion and argument that should have been spent rehearsing. Without Diaghileff the ballet would never have been completed.

"Of course it is difficult," he told Pat after he had been called into smooth over yet another quarrel. "A new, original creation is always full of difficulties. I remember when we did *Petrouchka* we had the same troubles. Fokine, who was to do the choreography, found the music so difficult that he said it was impossible to arrange dancing movements to it. Stravinsky refused to alter his music, and they would argue about it by the hour. In the end I managed to persuade Fokine that it could be done, that something great would come of it, so *Petrouchka* came through its difficulties and lived, just as *The Blue Train* will live. We shall overcome the obstacles."

It was during these stormy days that Pat realized fully where Diaghileff's own genius lay. It was by the power of his personality, by the unique mixture of bullying and charm, of brute force and tact, that he kept his difficult, brilliant team working together. No detail ever escaped him, but, at the same time, he never lost sight of the whole conception of the ballet. It was his impeccable taste and sure artistic sense that guided them, often in spite of themselves, to the finished whole, to the result that they all wanted. Music, scenery, costume, choreography, all had to be blended into a single and perfect work of art.

"We shall overcome the difficulties," Diaghileff had said, but even Pat began to wonder as he scrapped or altered one decor after the other as Laurens produced them, and Chanel's costumes were repeatedly changed or re-designed. So things went on, right up to the dress rehearsal, the day before the premiere of the ballet. Even then they were not finished. They had rehearsed in costume and, after it, the whole thing was torn to pieces again. Jean Cocteau ran about the auditorium in a mounting rage, shouting that this was wrong and that was wrong. Nijinska shouted back from the stage. There were storms and tears, and more alterations, and a further rehearsal for the next morning, a rehearsal that went on all the afternoon and right up to the moment when the stage hands arrived to set the scene for the first ballet of the evening.

"We must go through this new pas de deux once more." Nijinska led Pat away, and upstairs, in a large, empty dressing-room they rehearsed.

It was here Diaghileff found them. He did not interrupt until they had finished.

"Now, you have done enough." He came and put his arms around their shoulders. "You will rest. It will be all right tonight, you will see," but by that time they were almost too tired to care.

"I came to tell you," Diaghileff said to Pat, "there is someone in your dressing-room waiting to see you."

"Not another reporter," Pat groaned.

"No," Big Serge smiled at him, "not this time."

"Who is it then?"

"Go along and see."

Pat opened the door of his dressing-room and saw his dresser arranging a big basket of flowers on the table. There was someone else in the room too, on the sofa in the corner. She got up quickly as he came in.

"Pat, my darling!"

"Mother!" and he was hugging her tightly. She had come to see his success, and in the joy of that dear, familiar presence, the tiredness and worry all slipped away from him.

35

"The Blue Train"

FRIDAY JUNE, 20, 1924. The public were filling the theatre. It was a brilliant public. Diaghileff had drawn all the chic and the intellectual of Paris to the Théâtre des Champs Élysées this night.

The seats filled and programs rustled open. A classical ballet was to begin the evening. It would be followed by *Les Biches* and, lastly, the climax of the evening, *Le Train Bleu.*

In his dressing-room banked with flowers and smothered in telegrams, Anton Dolin, wrapped in a dressing-gown, paced to and fro wondering how he would live through the next hour and a half.

This walking about was no good he told himself; he must rest and relax. He flung himself on the sofa.

"Curtain up!" The call boy came around.

He pictured the scene out there, the crowded house, hushed to expectant silence, the immaculate black figure of the conductor outlined against the footlights, the orchestra watching that raised baton, and, in the wings, the dancers in classical white tutus, clustered like flowers, waiting.

Somehow the time passed. Soon now it would be his turn.

"I'm going to get dressed." Pat sprang up from the sofa.

His dresser brought out his costume. The bathing suit of the Beau Gosse had the deceptive simplicity of color and line that is the secret of the French chic. Pat tied and retied his shoes; whatever happened they must not come off.

He fidgeted with his make-up, he did unnecessary warming-up exercises. He went in to find Woizikowsky already dressed in his golfer's costume: plus fours, with pullover and socks of matching stripes.

The hands of the clock went slowly and remorselessly around. The dancers came up hot and sweating from *Les Biches*. Intermission now while the stage hands set the scene for *The Blue Train.*

The corps de ballet were changing quickly into the smart bathing costumes. Nijinska appeared in the passage in her white, short tennis frock.

"Where's my racket?" She sent people scurrying to and fro in a panic of searching.

Sokolova, in a bathing costume, came to find Pat.

"How are you, Duckie?"

"Awful."

"On stage for *The Blue Train,* please," the call boy chanted. They went down together.

"I wonder how Big Serge is feeling," said Sokolova as they stood on the side of the stage dipping their feet in the rosin tray.

They thought of him out there in his box, the big man with the monocle and the white streak in his hair. He was the only person that really mattered to them, the one person the company danced for, the man who had been the driving power bringing this moment into being. On this occasion, sitting next to him, in the place of honor, was a gray-haired lady in evening dress.

"Who is she?" people asked each other, but Mrs. Kay was unaware of the staring eyes. Her thoughts were all linked to her son's. She was sharing his first night hopes and fears. On the other side of Diaghileff sat Jean Cocteau. His face, under its shock of dark hair, was as pale as his shirt front. Nearby was big Darius Milhaud and his wife; Picasso too, with Olga. Chanel sat among her smart friends. There was Laurens with his wife. All the team in fact were in the house tonight, anxious and watchful, waiting for the moment when the curtain would rise on this new thing they had created.

While they waited the public read in their programs what Diaghileff himself had written about *The Blue Train*:

"The first point about *Le Train Bleu* is that there is no blue train in it. This being the age of speed it has already reached its destination and disembarked its passengers. These are to be seen on a beach, which does not exist, in front of a Casino which exists still less. Overhead passes an airplane which you do not see. And the plot represents nothing.

"Moreover this ballet is not a ballet, it is an operette dansé. The music is composed by Darius Milhaud, but it has nothing in common with the music which we associate with Darius Milhaud. It is danced by the real Russian ballet but it has nothing to do with the Russian ballet. It was invented for Anton Dolin, a classical dancer who does nothing classical. The scenery is painted by a sculptor, and the costumes are by a great arbiter of fashion who has never made a costume."

Strange words these that whetted the curiosity.

The house-lights faded. The conductor mounted his rostrum. This was the moment they had all been waiting for. The hush was intense.

As the first harsh chords of the overture to *The Blue Train* filled the house, the velvet curtains swung silently upwards, revealing, not the scene, but a painted drop curtain. On it, Picasso's modern brush had sent two massive surrealist figures with streaming hair racing across a tortured stormy background of rocks and sea. The feeling of the painting was matched by the strident, modern music which found its echo in the hearts of that modern audience.

The mood was set. Picasso's curtain rose on a bare and empty beach. Empty blue sky, empty, distant blue sea. Angular planes of rocks rising up on both sides. Two vast, modern fish standing on their heads. The whole scene was lit with brilliant, white sunshine.

A single dancer made his entrance and all over the house opera glasses were focused on him. No, it was not Dolin.

From behind the rocks, from behind the giant fish, came the others, the strolling, casual smart crowd of young people who thronged the beach with youth, color and movement. They smoked, and ground their cigarettes out under their heels. They looked at non-existent wrist watches. They stared at an invisible airplane passing overhead.

In the wings stood Anton Dolin, the bronzed and muscular Beau Gosse. His breathing was quick and fitful as he gathered himself for his entrance, feeling the force of energy in him rise to such a pressure that if he couldn't release it in his dance, his very heart would burst.

It was his music now. Someone was whispering something and he was on.

As he moved into the violent light of the projectors, a transformation took place. He felt light and strange as though he no longer belonged to himself, as though a spirit greater than he had taken control of his body telling it what to do, lifting him off the ground.

The public saw a young giant who seemed to tread on air. This muscular and athletic young man appeared to grow in stature before them as he whirled across the stage in cartwheels and overs. Up on his hands he went, on one hand. What a perfect control he had of that beautiful body of his. Applause followed him as he ran off. They wanted more. They would get it.

The Beau Gosse waited for his next entrance while Sokolova danced with Woizikowsky.

More applause as the corps de ballet borrowed a startling trick from the movies and danced in slow motion. How curiously effective it was.

The Beau Gosse again. Pas de deux with Nijinska. The swimmer and the tennis champion. Easy to see here that these two were classical dancers. What style and what grace they gave to these modern movements. The Beau Gosse had won over his audience. They waited eagerly for his next appearance. It was dramatic. Alone, he ran, and flung himself into the air, turning over. A thrill of horror ran through the house. He was falling, straight on to his back. No, he was up, on his toes, and doing the same thing. A series of sensational backfalls brought frenzied applause. Never before had a classical dancer been seen doing such things, and he did them with such polish and style.

The climax was still to come. Hidden in the wings stood a spring board. The music built up the moment. The crowd on the beach broke and grouped towards the rocks. A rising crescendo of chords drowned the sound of running feet and the take-off. The body of the Beau Gosse came hurtling through the air above their heads. It was a spectacular sight, and a thrill of fear shivered through those who watched, for below that flying body were the bare boards of the stage. His legs would be smashed to pieces when he landed.

People gasped. He was falling now, coming straight down on to his knees. How did he land? It was too quick to see. He was up on his toes, running forward. He was all right. Relief broke through in an outburst of applause.

The short half hour of *The Blue Train* had run its course. It was over. The dancers lined up for the bow, and the curtain rose again to the thunder of applause. The four principals stepped forward, then Dolin alone and a crescendo of enthusiasm brought the house to its feet calling out "Dolin! Dolin!" The stage was suddenly filled with laurel wreaths and flowers. Would the applause never end?

Up in the box Serge Diaghileff's hands reached out for Jean Cocteau and Mrs. Kay. The bold experiment had succeeded. It was the triumph of *The Blue Train* and the Ballet Russe, and the personal triumph of the dancer Anton Dolin. He had won Paris to his feet, and his name was made.

There he stood, in the center of the stage, a magnificent young dancer in all the glory and beauty of his nineteen years, still bowing and smiling. He turned now towards the box, his eyes seeking out the small figure of the one person in the world who mattered, his mother, whose steadfast belief had lighted him through all the darkness and doubt of his early years to this supreme moment.

"He is smiling to you." Big Serge leaned over to her, but Mrs. Kay could no longer see her famous son. The flower-filled stage had blurred, and her eyes were filled with tears of unbearable happiness. The shouting and the applause around her receded, and she was seeing her son Pat again through the groping years of his boyhood, through the years of courage and discipline that had led up to this triumph. Tonight a new dancer had been given to the world, and his mother knew that he had overtaken at last the vision that had haunted him for so long. With *The Blue Train,* the last veil had been pulled aside. Now clear and bright before him shone the glittering star of the destiny of Anton Dolin.